Atoms
and Icons

ATOMS AND ICONS

A Discussion
of the Relationships Between
Science and Theology

MICHAEL FULLER

MOWBRAY

Mowbray
A Cassell imprint
Wellington House,
125 Strand,
London,
WC2R 0BB
215 Park Avenue South,
New York, NY 10003

First published 1995

British Library Cataloguing-in-Publication Data

A catalogue record for this book is available from the British Library

ISBN 0–264–67383–2

Erratum
On the back cover, the address for the Church of St John the Evangelist should read
Princes Street, not Princess Street.

Typeset by Falcon Oast Graphic Art
Printed and bound in Great Britain by Biddles Ltd, Guildford and King's Lynn.

For

SUE

Contents

Foreword

In the past Christians have often denied new truth because they thought it contradicted their loyalty to Christ. This is the origin of the tragic split between science and religion, which goes as far back as Galileo, and was deepened by the Church's response to Darwin's hypothesis of the evolution of species. The 19th-century conflict over Drawin seriously disturbed a relationship that should have been close. Christianity has always been on the side of truth, wherever it came from. Simone Weil wrote some prophetic words to Father Perrin, Dominican Superior at Montpelier, in 1942: 'Christ likes us to prefer truth to him because, before being Christ, he is truth. If one turns aside from him to go towards the truth, one will not go far before falling into his arms.' One of the most encouraging and exciting facts of our own era is the way in which science and theology are again entering into dialogue with one another. The new science, especially the new physics, makes the debates of the 19th-century seem beside the point. Scientists and theologians at their best and most transparent are coming together to share the wonder they experience when they contemplate this extraordinary universe in which we are privileged to live for a season. Christianity in its essence should be catholic, universal in its generosity and intellectual excitement, but, as Simone Weil pointed out in the same letter, 'Christianity if catholic by right but not in fact. So many things are outside it, so many things that I love and do not want to give up, so many things that God loves, otherwise they would not be in existence.'

Michael Fuller is a scientist, a theologian and a parish priest and he is not content to let the many things that Simone Weil talked about be outside the love of God. In this fascinating and readable book he gives us a brilliant account of the current state of discussion between science and theology, demonstrating that there is no necessary contradiction between them, and, indeed, that there is a remarkable affinity. Appropriately he has called his book *Atoms and Icons*, because we are able to look both at things and through them, and that looking at and through becomes the wonder that is not necessary prelude to God's self-revelation.

† Richard Holloway
Bishop of Edinburgh

Preface

Apologies and leaky buckets

This is a book about religion – more specifically, about Christianity – and about science. To write such a book may be to make two mistakes in one: I dare say that many people open a book about science with only a little less reluctance than they open one about religion! However, I shall be referring only occasionally to the sort of devotional topics that the word 'religion' might lead you to expect, and hardly at all to the rather complex mathematics that underlies much serious science. This is because I am seeking to examine first and foremost the ways in which these two subjects interrelate, and it seems to me that when we pursue a discussion between two disciplines of thought in this way, the specialized thinking of one or the other can often be rather more of a hindrance than a help.

Why bother with a dialogue such as that between science and religion in the first place? It is my profound belief that science can, and should, inform the ways in which we 'think religiously'; and in addition, I believe that Christianity can and should be engaged with contemporary scientific and philosophical issues in the world in which Christians live, hopefully to the benefit of all concerned. This sort of approach – talking about religious issues in such a way as to forge links between them and more 'secular' views – has a long history. It has given rise to a type of literature which is sometimes referred to as 'Apologetic' writing. This does not mean that I feel I have something to be apologetic about: rather, this word is being used in a technical sense, to mean that I am writing what I hope is a *defence* of the faith which I profess.[1] My aim in this book is to set alongside each other the understandings of the world and of humankind that may be derived from the sciences and from Christian religious belief, in order to point out that there is actually a good deal of coherence between them. I also want to urge that we can learn from them both, and that respect is due to them both.

What I shall *not* be doing, I hasten to add, is seeking in some sense to 'prove' the truth of Christianity, or the existence of God. I do not believe that either of these are actually capable of proof. Nor shall I be attempting to 'prove' that science, or scientists, are in some sense wrong. This is something I should not particularly want to do, even if I believed it to be possible. What I want to do falls somewhere between these two extremes. I want to point out that the more extravagant claims made by those who support exclusively 'scientific' or 'religious' understandings of the world are unhelpful – as are the counter-claims of those who attack them. I believe that truth is to be sought not in claiming that only one or other of these two fields of human experience and endeavour is of relevance: this is the approach of the fundamentalist in either area. Rather, we should seek for the truth by combining the insights of both scientific and religious world-views.

This leads me to my title, 'Atoms and Icons'. These are two subjects not normally mentioned in the same breath, but in doing so it is my intention to bring together with a jolt two 'worlds' of thinking that we tend to keep firmly apart from one another in our minds. I hope that this book will be full of such jolts, and that many of the assumptions that are all too often made about the incompatibility of science and religion will thereby be challenged.

The arguments I shall be putting forward are not cast-iron and watertight (to mix metaphors). I do not believe such arguments to be appropriate to this area. Instead, the remarks I shall make are perhaps to be likened to leaky buckets. They will 'hold water' up to a certain point, but they are by no means totally irrefutable. The point about such buckets is that, if sufficient numbers of them are put together, they produce an argument that may be rather more persuasive than any one of the arguments in question by itself: the combination of all the arguments together may produce something that can 'hold water' after all. Such a 'leaky bucket' argument may sound like a rather non-rigorous way of proceeding; but, when all is said and done, most of the arguments that we use, outside the region of pure logic and mathematics, are of this type. In most other areas of our lives we put together a world-view we find persuasive on the basis of all the evidence at our disposal. Just how watertight we judge the combination of leaky buckets to be can, at bottom, only be a personal matter, based on our experiences of life, our feelings, and our prejudices. My request of the readers of this book is that he or she lay aside any such prejudices concerning the relationship between religion and science until the end of the book, and then assess with a fresh mind the assorted evidence – the combinations of leaky buckets – that I shall be presenting.

About what follows

In general, this book focuses on issues where science and religion are often seen to be opposed to each other in terms of their thinking, their methods, or their conclusions. I shall be looking at such issues as what it means to know something, rather than to believe it: the different models of human beings provided by scientific and by religious understandings of humanity: the sources used by the two disciplines of science and theology: the concepts used by each and the language used to talk about those concepts; and the understandings which exist within these two disciplines of such things as history, myth, tradition and authority. I shall maintain that the differences between the scientific and theological outlooks towards issues such as these are not in fact as great as one might suppose, and are, in general, differences of scale rather than of kind.

Whether you hold to the Christian faith and wish to explore its meanings more fully, or whether you have some understanding of science but have hitherto not paid very much attention to religious matters, I hope that you will find this book both approachable and useful. I have consciously avoided using jargon, of whatever sort, wherever I possibly can. A glossary of terms that I have felt obliged to use may be found at the front of the book. In a couple of examples I have introduced a little mathematical and/or technical language; however, if you wish to skip these sections, the flow of the book should not be disrupted.

I have used numbered references at intervals in the text, which direct the reader to the notes printed at the end of each chapter. The notes refer to books from which quotations and examples are taken, and give suggestions for further reading. They also sometimes expand slightly on the text. Much that makes fascinating reading has been written in the last few years on the topics that are covered in this book, to the extent that it should really be regarded only as an introduction to this whole area of study. I hope that the reader will be able to use these notes to follow up further any topics I discuss which he or she finds to be particularly interesting.

I'd like to make two points about the terminology which I use. First, it cannot be too strongly emphasized that God does not possess a gender. However, I (in common, I know, with many other theological writers) have found that it is virtually impossible to write of God using the English language avoiding totally the use of all gender-specific words. I have therefore taken the traditional way out, and when necessary I have used masculine pronouns and adjectives – 'he', 'him', 'his' – when speaking of God. The use of such terminology, however, should in no way be taken as an assumption that God's characteristics are any more male than female. Second, I have followed recent convention in replacing the abbreviations BC and AD, used with dates, by BCE and CE (standing respectively for 'Before Common Era' and 'Common Era'), which reflects more accurately the way in which this system of dating is used by all modern communities of thought, and not solely by Christian ones.

About the author

An author should perhaps say something about himself at the outset of a book, so that the reader understands a bit about where he or she is coming from. Let me therefore state that I am an Anglican clergyman, having attended a variety of Anglican churches from my late teens onwards. I studied chemistry at university, taking a doctorate for work in the field of synthetic organic chemistry. I then went on to take a degree in theology and to be ordained. At the time of writing this book, I was based in a parish in a large town in southern England.

As a result of all this, not only are the religious terms and concepts used in this book almost entirely Christian, but in addition the scientific examples I have chosen are frequently (although by no means exclusively) from the physical sciences (physics and chemistry) rather than the biological or 'human' sciences (biology, archaeology, anthropology, psychology, sociology, and so on). I hope, however, that much of what I have to say will be approachable for those with little or no background in either of these areas.

Acknowledgements

I dare say that I share with many of my readers an aversion to those awful, insincere-sounding 'Thank you' speeches, in which everyone is thanked from the speaker's parents to his or her hairdresser. The thank yous at the beginning of a book almost inevitably end up similar in appearance. Nevertheless, I would like to thank most sincerely the many people without whom this book could not have happened.

My parents have indeed been a great source of support and encouragement all along. My colleagues in the Society of Ordained Scientists have been a greater source of support than any of them will have realized. Frank Hillebrand and the people of All Saints', High Wycombe, and my students at the Chiltern Christian Training Programme, all had various ideas in this book tried out on them, and didn't complain unduly. Judith Longman, of

Mowbray, read the entire book in draft form, and offered much encouragement and many helpful comments. Derek Edwards, Arthur Peacocke, Joanna Sandbach and Justin Wark also generously read all of the book in draft form, and Mark Philpott read part of it. Subsequent conversations with them, and the written criticisms which they offered, were all most helpful. To Dr Peacocke I am especially grateful for his many helpful comments and for the time which he made available to give them. My wife Sue offered all the help and support that I could possibly have asked for in the course of the writing of this book. Needless to say, after all this attention any remaining deficiencies (or, indeed, excesses) are entirely my own responsibility. Thank you very much, all of you.

And finally, thank you also Terry – the best barber in Buckinghamshire.

MJF, March 1995

NOTES

1. 'Apologetic' literature goes right back to pre-Christian times, in fact. Plato's account of the speech of Socrates defending himself at his trial is titled his 'Apology': it is a title evoked subsequently in the early Christian era by Christians called upon to defend themselves and their faith. The most notable early Christian apologist is perhaps Justin Martyr, who was executed in Rome in about the year 165 CE. Justin's writings, available in volume 1 of *The Ante-Nicene Fathers* (T. & T. Clark, reprinted 1989), make fascinating reading for anyone interested in the early interactions of Christians with the secular culture of their day.

1

By way of introduction . . .

The last thing one discovers in composing a work is what to put first.

Blaise Pascal, *Pensées*

Science versus religion?

As I mentioned in the Preface, I used to be a research chemist, and I am now a priest. This statement doesn't strike me as particularly remarkable: there are so many ordained scientists in this country (and beyond) that we even have our own Society. However, it constantly provokes surprise, interest and sometimes even bewilderment in the people I meet. Similarly, when a lectureship devoted to the study of the relationship between science and theology was recently endowed at Cambridge University, a bemused, even astonished, reaction was reported from many quarters. Why is it that such surprise appears to be the norm?

I believe that this surprise is often due to people having a view of the 'worlds' of science and religion which sees them as rivals, or even as antagonists, in claiming people's loyalties. This view would presume that anyone saying they are committed to one 'world' can have little interest in the other, and might even regard it as hostile. I am convinced that this view is utterly wrong, and that the overlaps and similarities between the worlds of science and religion are in fact many in number, and profound in consequence.

A few caricatures

It is also noticeable in today's world that the activities and opinions

1

of the scientist often command considerable respect, and sometimes even reverence. On the other hand, the activities and views of the religious believer, whether the academic theologian, the church minister, or the ordinary churchgoer, receive little attention and are apparently assumed to be of interest solely to a slightly eccentric minority. Clearly this was not always the case: not so very long ago the situation was completely reversed. A mere few decades ago scientists were frequently caricatured as eccentric 'boffins', whose activities were as likely to prove dangerous as they were beneficial, whilst the Church was held to be the bastion of sound and sensible, 'right-thinking' people. Of course, those caricatures were both every bit as false as the present-day ones; but a switch in public opinion is nevertheless apparent.

To stay with caricatures for a moment, it seems to me that the view of religious believers – Christian or otherwise – put about by the mass media all too often divides such believers into two groups. On the one hand, there are more or less 'fundamentalist' fanatics. These, it is alleged (or at least implied), adhere to pretty implausible doctrines, and have an 'I'm right – you're wrong' kind of attitude towards the rest of the world, in whatever language that attitude may be expressed ('saved/damned', for example). On the other hand, there are those who are more cautious about such simplistic views: they often assert that past understandings of religious belief need to be re-examined. Their wish to question is frequently confused with a lack of conviction, and so they end up being labelled as heretics or doubters for their pains.

For example, contrast the sort of media attention given to the likes of Morris Cerullo, and similar American fundamentalists and 'televangelists', with that given to David Jenkins, who was until recently the Bishop of Durham, and similar theological thinkers. The first are treated as frauds playing on the emotions of the gullible, the second as dangerous radicals seeking to undermine people's faith. Scorn is poured on both, and seldom in either case is any real effort made to understand what exactly they are trying to do. Undoubtedly the intolerance, dogmatism and avarice of some fundamentalists, and the occasional obscurity or provocativeness of some academic theologians, do play a part in generating these sorts of media images. In many cases, however, it would appear rather that media correspondents are simply on the look-out for a story, and have little or no interest in any serious issues or debates which may underlie it. Of course, there is nothing new in this; and in a sense it is hardly surprising that an organization like the Church, which urges its followers to turn the other cheek to their opponents, will never be short of detractors in search of an easy target. Indeed, this has probably always been the case.[1]

The religious believer seems to be caught in something of a cleft stick here. The message that all too often emerges from this sort of coverage of religious issues is that one cannot be both a genuine believer and think seriously and rigorously through the consequences of one's belief. A third aim of this book is therefore to attempt to put to rest this sort of 'either–or' caricature. Taking part in serious theological discussion is not only possible, it is *essential* for the thoughtful believer who wants to develop his or her faith. And even those who do not profess a religious faith may find it interesting!

The popularity of science

Science continues to have a tremendous popular appeal in our day. Having said that, scientific research may not perhaps be viewed with quite the naïve enthusiasm that it once attracted. It is frequently very expensive, and at a time when resources are limited, its value may sometimes be questioned. In addition, the environmental hazards posed by some scientific research have been given considerable publicity, and are rightly generating a great deal of concern. However, science has unquestionably done a great deal of good in our world, and I believe it has the potential to do a great deal more. I should therefore like to state categorically that what I am *not* trying to do is to dismiss or under-rate the achievements of science.

Having said that, though, the reverential and uncritical attitude that some people apparently have towards the sciences needs to be examined carefully. It is doubtless due at least in part to an understanding of science which sees it as explaining the apparent mysteries of the universe. Science is thereby seen as fulfilling our need to make sense of our surroundings. Paradoxically, I suspect that it is also due at least in part to the fact that science can provide alternative 'mysteries' to those of religions (through, for example, the inexplicable findings of quantum theory). It is therefore able to fascinate and stir people, and to fulfil the need we all have for such fascination and stirring. The remarkable proliferation over the last century or so of science fiction, some of it plausible, some of it not, bears witness to the remarkable appeal that science has for even the most unscientific of minds. It can be rather a depressing experience now to read the science fiction produced in the 1960s and 1970s, which could often be full of boundless optimism about the future that the applications of science and technology would be able to provide: our world can seem so grey when compared with the kind of future worlds that were being predicted then. Still, I suspect that that optimistic tone remains forever associated with science in the minds of those who have read such books, no matter how much more lacklustre and pedestrian today's scientific reality might be.

Scientists themselves can, of course, be very optimistic about their subject. Frank Tipler, a mathematical physicist (who professes also to be an atheist), is so positive about the potential of his discipline that he has even tried to extend it into the realm of theology. He has put forward a cosmological theory which, he believes, shows 'That we have free will, that God exists, and that he will one day resurrect each and every one of us to eternal life', and he has even gone so far as to claim that 'Theology is a branch of physics.'[2] Despite Tipler's enthusiasm, however, it need hardly be said that the explaining of such religious phenomena as these, or even (rather more modestly) the explaining of all the physical phenomena of the cosmos, is far from being a stated aim of the majority of practising scientists. Even those physicists who pursue the possibility of formulating a 'final theory', or 'theory of everything', to unite the many theories currently used within that discipline, tend to be cautious when considering what such a theory might achieve. Steven Weinberg, a physicist concerned with the quest for such a 'final theory', has suggested that:

> Various silly things ... might be meant by a final theory, as for instance that discovery of a final theory in physics would mark the end of science. Of course a final theory would not end scientific research, nor even pure research in physics. Wonderful phenomena, from turbulence to thought, will still need explanation whatever final theory is discovered. The discovery of a final theory in physics will not necessarily even help very much in making progress in understanding these phenomena (although it may with some).[3]

Similarly, the astronomer John Barrow writes: 'The scope of Theories of Everything is infinite but bounded; they are necessary parts of a full understanding of things but they are far from sufficient to unravel the subtleties of a Universe like ours.'[4]

I have suggested that in some respects the popular, optimistic view of science has taken on certain of the functions that religions once had. It gives people confidence that the world around them is comprehensible and controllable: it gives people a hope for a better future; and in its richness, complexity and frequent incomprehensibility from the non-scientist's point of view, it provides people with something to wonder at. I don't think that it's going too far to say that it re-introduces a certain mystery into people's view of the world.

Some caution is necessary here, however. This kind of 'mystery-making' using scientific language and ideas may be misused, in the same way that religious language and symbols may be misused deliberately to obscure things in order to make them sound or appear impressive. Here's an anecdote to show what I mean. I remember once being shown a bottle of shampoo, the label of which promised that it would 'Hydrolyze the keratin' in your hair. Sounds impressive, doesn't it? However, what it actually means is this. Keratin is the fibrous protein which constitutes hair. When a protein is hydrolyzed, it is broken up into the smaller molecules, called amino acids, of which it is made. Amino acids are soluble in water. What the label on this shampoo bottle actually *means*, therefore, is that the shampoo will make your hair dissolve. This is not, I assume, the meaning that its manufacturers intend to convey. This kind of 'blinding with science' is, under any circumstances, a most improper use of science. (To be fair, it is not something that scientists themselves do very often: it's usually done by those with commercial rather than scientific motives.)

Let's now return to our discussion of the perceived conflict between science and religion.

Why the supposed conflict?

I believe that the continued perception of science and religion as things which are radically different, even opposed, is frequently due to an outmoded, nineteenth-century understanding of both of these subjects. Twentieth-century understandings of how the physical world operates are very different to those of the last century, and twentieth-century philosophers of science have given us a very different view of the scientific enterprise – of what science is, and of how it is carried out – than the rather naïve understandings of their predecessors. Moreover, theologians have advanced considerably in their understandings of the Bible and of the way in which its writings have been developed and expanded by theological thinkers through centuries of Christian tradition. Our ideas about God, derived from the Bible and from those thinkers, are constantly changing. Why is it that these more modern understandings of both science and religion have not filtered down to become common currency amongst the majority of people?

Partly, perhaps, it is due to academic scientists and theologians not 'popularizing' these developments as much as·they might: the pressures on them are rather to publish work in specialist journals, which are read principally by others from their own field of study. However, much work *has* been explained at a 'popular' level by writers in both disciplines. It seems to me that the view of science and religion as totally opposed is, at bottom, a view perpetuated principally by fundamentalists on both sides.

Let me explain what I mean by the word 'fundamentalist'. Fundamentalists tend to assert that their more or less narrow view of the world is the sole correct one, and that all alternatives are to be rejected. They make little or no attempt to sympathize with those alternatives, or even to understand fully what they are. Evidence contrary to the fundamentalists' own viewpoint is totally and summarily dismissed as irrelevant or phoney. Fundamentalists seem to have an almost paranoid desire to maintain the sole authority of the world-view expressed by their own position, and they will frequently resort to crude rhetoric and the defamation of their opponents in place of logical argument (sometimes, it must be admitted, to good effect, when the fundamentalist concerned is a skilled rhetorician). Whence their paranoia arises is unclear: perhaps it derives from a sense of insecurity, or from the fundamentalist feeling a loss of power in a world which tolerates many views in addition to the fundamentalist's own.

Here are examples of writings by scientific and religious fundamentalists, in both cases touching on the theory of evolution, which for some reason is still often seen as a case where scientific and religious understandings are necessarily and implacably opposed. First, the scientific fundamentalist view. Richard Dawkins, a well-known biologist, has written:

> What, after all, is faith? It is a state of mind that leads people to believe something – it doesn't matter what – in the total absence of supporting evidence. If there were good supporting evidence then faith would be superfluous, for the evidence would compel us to believe it anyway. It is this that makes the often-parroted claim that 'evolution itself is a matter of faith' so silly. People believe in evolution not because they arbitrarily want to believe it but because of overwhelming, publicly available evidence.[5]

Here we see a good example of the sort of fundamentalist intolerance that I mentioned, and also the setting up of 'either–or' alternatives. Either one accepts 'overwhelming' evidence, or one ignores it and plumps instead for a totally irrational 'faith'. However, I would maintain against Dawkins, that few things, if any, may be believed without at least a measure of faith: that there is for most 'believers' plenty of evidence to support their faith, even if it is not always easy to communicate that evidence to another person; and that there *is* actually an objective arbitrariness to what most people choose to believe, even if it is an arbitrariness directed by the personal experiences of the individual concerned (what evidence you or I find to be 'overwhelming' may vary considerably, depending on what we actually *want* to believe). These issues will be discussed more fully later in this book. Dawkins is a passionate (and, it may be added, extremely clever and skilful) advocate of his own preferred set of beliefs, which centre on Darwinism; and there is undoubtedly a great deal of 'publicly available evidence' to support his position. Similar evidence is also available to support many other positions, on this and other topics.

Incidentally, this comment by Dawkins is inserted into his book at a point where he himself makes 'the often-parroted claim' that religious belief (and also patriotic and political beliefs) are responsible for atrocities like religious persecutions, the crusades and the activities of contemporary terrorists. Is it necessary to reiterate once again the point that this is true, if only in the sense that it is also true that science is similarly responsible for the uranium and hydrogen bombs, the economic and technological oppression of 'Third World' countries, and pollution on such a massive scale that the very ecosystem of our planet is threatened by it? What is at issue here is surely not religion or science *per se*, but, rather, the selfish exploitation of religion or of science by unscrupulous individuals or societies, heedless of the responsibilities that both religion and science should engender. Many scientists were, naturally enough, appalled at the potential power of the uranium bomb. Similarly, I would maintain, those who profess a religious belief can only be appalled at any atrocities which are committed in its name. Such atrocities are, after all, so clearly contrary to the basic teachings of virtually every major religion, since all of them urge the way of peace upon their followers.

I suspect that Dawkins' writing is inspired to a significant extent by his passionate opposition to the sort of religious fundamentalism which, particularly in the United States of America, has lobbied successfully to restrict the teaching of evolution in schools and colleges. This is doubtless why he himself has similarly been urging recently that theology should not be taught in the universities of this country. Intemperate views will, of course, always inspire intemperate opposition: incidentally, it is rather amusing in this context to see Dawkins write that he finds the criticisms of a philosopher who has opposed him 'highly intemperate and vicious', apparently blissfully unaware that others might perceive his own writings in the same light.[6] I agree fully with him that the situation in America is deplorable, though I would urge that his solution – to fight repression with repression – is hardly the best one. The idea that dictatorial restrictions should be placed on what may and may not be regarded as a valid field of academic enquiry is surely utterly unworthy of one who claims to speak as a scientist. It is salutory to note how sharply Dawkins' strident assertions of the powers of his science contrast with the rather greater humility shown by the physicists quoted above concerning the possibilities of constructing a 'theory of everything'.

Compare the rhetoric of Dawkins with the following example of religious fundamentalism, from a book published by the Jehovah's Witnesses:

> We need to face the fact that the theory of evolution serves the purposes of Satan . . . How, then, should we feel about this? We feel indignant toward those who try to defraud us of money, or even of a few material possessions. We should feel even stronger indignation toward the doctrine of evolution and its originator, since the intent is to defraud us of eternal life.[7]

This is fundamentalist intolerance of the opposite sort to that of Dawkins, and it is just as unhelpful. Again, we see displayed the intemperate use of language, and condemnation of opponents: again, we see the setting up of an 'either–or' pair of alternatives – in this case, either one rejects the theory of evolution or one 'serves the purposes of Satan', and, presumably, is defrauded of eternal life in consequence. Again, as with Dawkins, clearly the intention of the polemic is to refute an opposing view that is seen as dangerous – in this particular case, the theory of evolution as supporting atheism (which, in any case, I do not believe it necessarily does). The book this quotation is taken from makes a few valid points about the current incompleteness of evolutionary theory; but to leap from these to the conclusion quoted seems to me extraordinary, and, indeed, positively dangerous in the militant antagonism of its outlook. The violent and emotive language used can never be helpful in the context of a serious argument. Needless to say, many religious thinkers would repudiate this sort of thinking about scientific matters, just as many scientific thinkers would repudiate the theological thinking of Dawkins.

I personally find fundamentalists – both religious and scientific – rather sad, since I think that both miss so much. I suspect that they have in common a psychological make-up that is incapable of living with doubt or uncertainty. This means that they see all world-views which might be considered to be in any sense opposed to their own as dangerous things, which have to be railed against whenever possible. Whilst I myself am sometimes tempted to rail about some things that I feel strongly about, this is a temptation I shall try to resist. One can only agree with Sallie McFague's comment that 'Balance often qualifies insight out of existence.'[8] Nevertheless, I have tried to temper my own opinions with a careful and balanced approach to their presentation. It is the cautious liberal's fate to risk being unexciting in the attempt to be scrupulous: on balance, however, I prefer to run that risk rather than simply to write opinionated polemic.

A word about definitions

One phrase that will recur constantly as a refrain through this book is, 'What do we mean by ...?' I make no apologies for this, since I think it is of great importance that we define carefully, wherever possible, the concepts we are discussing. Some of the definitions we shall arrive at may be surprising.

It also needs to be said, however, that where abstract ideas are concerned, we can frequently never arrive at a totally satisfying and complete definition of them. Consider a term like 'postmodernism', a word greatly in vogue recently. It seems to me to be incapable of straightforward definition: we simply have to use it when we feel it appropriate, observe the variety of circumstances under which other people use it, and gradually assimilate more and more of its meaning by setting up an interconnected 'web' of associations around the word. Through its use, the meaning of the word then gradually begins to unfold itself. Words like 'God', 'religion', even 'science', also cannot easily be defined: they need to be used, and their uses by other people observed, for a network of relationships to be built up around them, enabling something of their meaning to be communicated. Sometimes, then, I may use words without defining them carefully: I hope that what I mean by them will become apparent as my argument progresses.

Religion and theology

Let me at this point raise a 'What do we mean by ...?' question, specifically, 'What do we mean by the words "religion" and "theology"?' Both these words have already been used, and I'd like to say a little bit more about them – and I also hope thus to explain a little more about what this book is and is not attempting to do. 'Religion' is a word describing a system by which a person orientates his or her life. This system is not simply a belief system, but rather more than that. It will, in all probability, provide models for personal behaviour, rules for social behaviour, solace in time of need, and perhaps some explanations of the internal and external phenomena which are experienced by the believer. The existence of a god or gods may be asserted by the system in order to account for some of these things, or to lend importance to its understanding of them.

Some of these things may readily be described to someone who is outside the system in question. For example, some social–ethical codes of religions may easily be stated in ways that anyone can understand: it is not difficult for a person who does not profess faith to understand – and, indeed, to uphold – the message of the Ten Commandments: do not steal, do not kill, and so on. Other things may not be so readily communicated to the outsider by the adherent of the system.

In addition to the objective, legal part of a religious system, there will usually be an element of personal conviction, based on personal experience, that cannot readily be communicated in objective terms: or which is perhaps capable of alternative interpretation when it is so expressed. A believer in God will often speak of his or her experiences of God; but these are likely to be subjective experiences which the outsider is quite at liberty to explain in other ways – as hallucination, self-delusion, the product of extreme physical or emotional tiredness, or whatever. Because of this, the present book will not be addressing such phenomena as these. The personal component of religion will not be examined in any detail, despite the fact that it is a vital – in the most literal sense of that word – and integral part of religion.

Similarly 'theology'. Theology has been poetically described as 'Faith seeking understanding':[9] it means, essentially, the study of God. One commentator has expressed the distinction between religion and theology thus: 'One of [man's] characteristic activities is the exercise of religion . . . Theology is the intellectual analysis of that specific human activity.'[10] Theology is essentially an intellectual exercise. However, like religion, theology may be said to have objective and subjective parts: that is to say, some aspects which may easily be expressed in terms that mean more or less the same to you as they do to me, and some aspects which I may understand in ways that I cannot readily and unambiguously communicate to you. We may examine the theories of who God is, and the arguments for and against the existence of God, in a relatively impersonal way; but any believer in God will also in part depend on extra material in the way of personal experiences which are of importance in his or her understanding of these theories or resolution of these arguments. The great spiritual traditions, dealing with the variety of subjective and personal ways in which human beings have approached God, are vitally important in the contribution that they make to our theological understandings. However, we shall only be considering them briefly in what follows. To leave out the personal experiences which vitally underpin so much religious and theological understanding may seem odd, but I hope that the gain in the general relevance of what I'm trying to say will offset this loss.

Having looked briefly at what we mean by 'religion' and by 'theology',

I should now like to address the question, 'What do we mean by science?' This task will be undertaken in the next chapter.

NOTES

1. The command to Christians to 'Turn the other cheek' goes back to Jesus himself (Matthew 5. 39). Clearly, the Church gained a reputation early on for being vulnerable to exploitation by the unscrupulous. The Roman writer Lucian tells of a charlatan named Peregrinus Proteus who imposed himself on Christians around the middle of the second century CE, receiving goods and money from them (*On the Death of Peregrinus*, 11–16). A fascinating early Christian writing, the *Didache* (probably written around the end of the first century CE), explicitly warns Christians not to be taken in by con-men (*Didache*, ch. 12).
2. These extraordinary statements occur in Frank J. Tipler's book *The Physics of Immortality* (Macmillan, 1995), p. 2 and p. ix. In this work, Tipler defines 'a living being' as 'Any entity which encodes information . . . with the information coded being preserved by natural selection. Thus "life" is a form of information processing, and the human mind – and the human soul – is a very complex computer program' (p. 124). He therefore sees 'immortality' in terms of the persistence of the information content encoded in such an entity, by that information being transferred to some other piece of computer 'hardware'. 'Resurrection' simply involves the running elsewhere of the programs which are encoded in our brains.

    Noting the incursions made by physicists into the realms of cosmology which have in the past been dealt with by theologians, Tipler also makes the delightful assertion that 'Theological research in the twenty-first century will require a Ph.D. in particle physics' (p. 329), remarking (quite correctly) that in medieval times theology was studied only *after* the prospective student had already mastered the best philosophy of the day.
3. S. Weinberg, *Dreams of a Final Theory* (Vintage, 1993), p. 13.
4. J. D. Barrow, *Theories of Everything* (Vintage, 1992), p. 210.
5. Richard Dawkins, *The Selfish Gene* (Oxford University Press, 2nd edition, 1989), p. 330.
6. Dawkins, *ibid.*, p. 278.
7. *Life – How Did it Get Here?* (Watchtower Bible and Tract Society of New York, Inc., 1985), p. 248.
8. Sallie McFague, *The Body of God* (SCM Press, 1993), p. ix.
9. This expression was coined in the eleventh century by St Anselm, in his *Proslogion* (see, e.g. *The Prayers and Meditations of St Anselm*, trans. Benedicta Ward (Penguin, 1973), pp. 238 ff.).
10. A. Peacocke, *Intimations of Reality: Critical Realism in Science and Religion* (University of Notre Dame Press, 1984), p. 36.

2

Believing and knowing

'Scientists don't claim to be infallible ... it's really we laymen who attach infallibility to their statements.'
'For heaven's sake, stop this philosophy, Francis.'
Fred Hoyle, *The Black Cloud*

Belief and knowledge

It's often thought that religions are based on believing and the sciences on knowing. If the two activities of believing and knowing are somehow fundamentally different from each other, then this would indicate a major difference between the religious and the scientific understandings of the world. I therefore now want to examine what we mean by the words 'belief' and 'knowledge'. This may appear at first glance to be plunging us into areas of philosophy remote from both science and theology, but I hope that my reasons for taking our discussion into these fields will soon become clear.

These days, the word 'believers' has come to have almost a pejorative meaning: it is as though such people do not think clearly. If they did, they wouldn't have to entrust themselves to belief, or superstition, or whatever. This seems to be the way in which Richard Dawkins understands this word, as we have seen. Belief is sometimes explicitly contrasted with 'knowledge', as though they were opposite poles of human understanding. Knowledge tends to be a word with rather more positive associations than belief. On the one hand, knowledge is something of which one can be certain, something universal, something that can be trusted; whilst on the other hand, belief is more vague, more personal, more subjective, and hence more unreliable. The difference between the two is perceived as being almost as acute as that between fact and fiction. 'Science', the very name of which actually comes from a Latin verb meaning 'to know', can consequently claim a great deal of authority for itself, since the scientific endeavour is held to generate knowledge; and one who speaks as a 'scientist' is usually given a considerable amount of respect in consequence.

In actual fact, however, the distinction between belief and knowledge is not quite as clear cut as you might think from the ways in which we commonly use those words. Many philosophers in recent years have studied what is meant by the scientific method (that is, the way in which scientists construct their experiments, carry out their measurements, and analyse their results), and many have suggested that this method has boundaries and limitations in terms of the certainty of the knowledge which it can generate. Not only that, but the actual doing of science involves the scientists concerned making various suppositions which might themselves be more or less 'scientific'. No experiment can be conducted in a theoretical vacuum: scientists *expect* to observe some things and not others, and construct experiments accordingly. Moreover, scientific investigations themselves reveal that there are things in the physical word about which science is *necessarily* ignorant: put simply, it can be shown that there are some things that we just *cannot* ever know.

So, let's begin to address the questions 'What do we mean by belief?' and 'What do we mean by knowledge?' by asking 'What do we mean by science?', since science is widely held to be that discipline which generates knowledge, and in the practice of which belief is generally reckoned to be unnecessary.

What is science?

When we consider the physical sciences, it seems to me that the view of them which persists in many people's minds today is derived from a nineteenth-century *materialist* understanding of the universe. ('Materialism', incidentally, is used here in a technical sense to refer to the idea that all that is to be accounted of significance is matter, the physical stuff of which the cosmos is made: the idea that there is no such thing as 'spirit', or indeed anything else, apart from matter.) This 'nineteenth-century' understanding of science attributes five special features to it which, together, distinguish it from all other spheres of human activity.

1. It is *deterministic*. This means that events are determined – fixed – through the chains of cause and effect that have led up to them. One nineteenth-century scientist, named Laplace, said that if one knew all the positions and momenta of every particle in the universe simultaneously, together with the laws governing their movements and interactions, one would be able to predict the entire past and future course of history. This is an extreme statement of determinism, the idea being that *everything* is theoretically predictable in terms of straightforward physical laws. It follows, of course, that concepts like free will – the observation that human beings do things of their own volition, because they *want* to do them – are in fact illusions. All that we do is in fact determined by the behaviour of the molecules in our bodies, and by the physical laws which govern the way in which they interact with each other.

2. It is *inductive*. This means that the scientist proceeds by gathering data, many practical (or, as we sometimes say, 'empirical') observations of what happens in the physical world, for example through carrying out experiments in a laboratory. From these data the scientist then constructs a general theory that takes account of, and explains, them all (or, at least, as many of them as possible).

3. It is *rational*. This means that only logical thought processes are considered to have any part to play in scientific procedures. The use of our imaginations or of intuition, for example, is not considered to be a scientific way to proceed.

4. It is *objective*. This means that if I perform an experiment, it will yield the same results as it would if you were to do the same experiment under the same conditions. Scientific information does not depend upon who is doing the experiment.

5. It is *reductionist*. This means that explanations of how things behave is to be looked for in terms of the behaviour and interactions of the parts of which they are made. The behaviour of living organisms, say, is to be explained in terms of the cells of which they are made: the behaviour of cells is to be explained in terms of the operations of the complex organic chemicals (proteins, lipids, nucleic acids and so on) of which they, in turn, are made: the behaviour of these complex chemicals is to be understood in terms of the simpler molecules which constitute them: the behaviour of these molecules is to be understood in terms of the atoms which in turn constitute them: the behaviour of atoms is to be understood in terms of the sub-atomic particles of which they are made; and so on.

In short, the reductionist principle is that the behaviour of whole things is governed by the behaviour of their parts.

All five of these assumptions have been challenged by modern philosophers of science. Let's look one at a time at what has been said about them.

Determinism

Most people are taught at school about the laws governing the collisions between bodies in motion. These laws were originally discovered by Sir Isaac Newton, and they have his name attached to them – Newton's laws. They are very successful indeed in predicting what will happen in many physical systems in motion – the motions of the planets around the sun, for example. Now, ultimately the entire universe is comprised of countless bodies in motion, from stars and planets at one end of the scale to molecular, atomic and sub-atomic particles at the other. Moreover, all physical entities in the universe, including living ones, may also be said to be comprised of such bodies in motion. (You and I are made of complex organic chemicals – chemicals based on the element carbon – which are made of simpler molecules, which are made of atoms, and so on . . .). It is therefore obviously a great temptation to infer that the behaviour of all physical entities, including the behaviour of all living organisms, within any closed system in the universe, up to and including the universe itself in its entirety, may (theoretically at least) be inferred from a knowledge of the initial conditions of that system together with a knowledge of all the physical laws (such as Newton's laws) which are applicable to it. This understanding of the physical world lies behind Laplace's assertion about the predictability of the entire history of the universe, as mentioned above.

However, there are two problems with this. The first comes with measurement. If we are to gather information of this sort about molecular and smaller systems, then we must do so by measuring them; and there will always be an element of inaccuracy in any measurements that we are able to make. The effects of this are dramatically illustrated in the following example. Consider a system of a very large number of colliding balls, like balls on a snooker table, which are set in motion by one ball, and which then continue in motion indefinitely, each one hitting the next and rebounding from it without losing energy in the process. This was the sort of system that Laplace was thinking about when he made the suggestion that I mentioned above: it is also the same sort of system which scientists imagine when theorizing about what are called 'ideal' gases. In this kind of system, if all the initial conditions of the system are known, together with the laws which govern the interactions of the particles (in this case

Newton's laws, which the balls may be assumed to obey), then all the future states of the system should, indeed, be theoretically predictable.

However, such a system as this is highly sensitive to the angles of impact between the balls. It has been shown that if the average distance between the balls is ten times their radius, then an error of one digit in the nth place of decimals in the angle of impact of the first collision means that after n collisions all certainty in the directions of the balls is lost. In other words, if the initial angle of impact were known to an accuracy of one in the 1000th decimal place (which sounds pretty accurate, doesn't it?), then after 1000 collisions one would not know whether any particular ball was moving in one direction, or in another direction at right angles to it. There will *always*, inevitably, be some error, however small, in our ability to measure such things as this. Thus, even in a system that obeys Newton's laws, uncertainty creeps in – such a system may never be known by us completely, for purely practical reasons. Even more extraordinarily, even if the angle of the first collision were known exactly, unpredictability would still arise in this system, since it cannot be considered apart from the universe in which it is located. It transpires that a factor as small as the gravitational force exerted by an electron at the far side of the observable universe would render this system of colliding balls unpredictable within a matter of a minute or so.[1] Laplace's vision is demonstrably one which it is completely beyond our powers to attain.

In addition to this practical problem, there is a theoretical one. Quantum physics has demonstrated that in very small systems – atomic and sub-atomic systems, for example – there are some things which simply cannot be known simultaneously, such as, for example, the position and momentum of a single particle. The greater the accuracy with which one of these things is known, the greater the uncertainty in the accuracy with which the other can be known: if the position of a particle is known with 100 per cent accuracy, then absolutely nothing can be known about its momentum, and vice versa. (This is known as Heisenberg's Uncertainty Principle.) This being the case, once again Laplace's deterministic theory is shown to be hopelessly idealistic. It must include in its reckoning the behaviour of very small systems, but it assumes a knowledge of such systems which, we can actually demonstrate, will necessarily always be denied us. Similarly, 'chaos theory', which has received a great deal of attention recently, has demonstrated that there are systems which, although they can be described by deterministic equations, yet reveal an incredible sensitivity to initial conditions; and this makes their behaviour to all intents and purposes unknowable to us in practice. (Technically speaking, such systems as this are described as being *ontologically* deterministic but *epistemologically* non-deterministic: they are essentially determined by the equation defining them, but they are non-deterministic in terms of what it is possible for us to know about them.)[2]

The inductive method

You will remember that induction is the process of reasoning from many observations to a general theory, which is considered to be 'proved' by them. The underlying assumption of this method is that future observations will continue to confirm the theory in question. However, an eighteenth-century Scottish philosopher named David Hume pointed out long ago that induction as a method is logically flawed, because of this very assumption that something that has been observed to happen under certain conditions in the past will necessarily always happen again in the future. You may think that this is nit-picking somewhat; but in fact it is a fundamental truth that there can be no way of *proving* that something that has happened in the past will always happen again in the future. The events of the future are always hidden from us, as there is a fundamental asymmetry to time. In addition, events of the past cannot ever be precisely reproduced in the future, since other events will always have taken place that render this impossible.

A philosopher named Karl Popper – generally reckoned to be the most important and influential philosopher of science of this century – took on board all that Hume had said about the method of induction, and in doing so he radically changed our understanding of science. It was previously assumed that since science is, after all, a quest for knowledge, then a scientific fact must be one which has been proved to be true. Not so, said Popper, since (as we have seen) induction can never *prove* that anything that has happened in the past will necessarily happen again in the future. Given this, in answer to the question 'What is science?' Popper came up with a radically new means of distinguishing between science and non-science (a *criterion of demarcation*, as it is known): the criterion of *falsifiability*. A scientific theory, as opposed to a non-scientific one, is not a theory that *has* been proved *true*, but rather one which *may* be proved *false*. So, a theory regarding, for example, the structure of an atomic nucleus, may have hypotheses deduced from it which can be tested experimentally, and the theory may be proved false as a result of those experiments. It may therefore be considered a scientific theory. On the other hand, a theory about, say, the existence of souls, cannot be tested in a practical way, cannot therefore be falsified, and so (according to Popper) is not scientific. The proposed model of scientific method is therefore one of *conjecture and refutation* (to borrow the title of one of Popper's books). Rather than proceed by induction – moving from specific examples to a general conclusion – Popper suggests that science has to proceed by deduction – moving from a general theory, which is a pure conjecture, to a specific refutation of that theory.[3]

Now, if we are to follow this method, we would make various observations and on the basis of them we would arrive at a theory T1, which (we feel) satisfactorily explains them. T1 enables us to make predictions, and to set up experiments to test those predictions. The observations made in the course of these experiments may confirm our belief that T1 is a good theory, which it would be if it were able to explain these new observations as satisfactorily as it did the old ones. On the other hand, the new observations may contradict some feature of T1, and mean that we have to revise it to a new theory, T2, the revision necessary being more or less drastic depending on the nature of the new evidence. So far, so good. However, where does all this leave us in our quest for knowledge, or for truth? We thought at one point that T1 was true: now all that we can say is that it represented a state of affairs which we believed to be true at a particular moment in time. The fate of T2 is equally uncertain: in due course, as more experiments are performed and more data are gathered, the chances are that it will itself be superseded by a new theory T3, and so on. So where does this leave us in any quest for absolute truth? Is it possible to have a scientifically *proven* fact at all?

Fascinatingly, Popper maintains that *it isn't*. The scientific quest is not for fact, for a full and complete *knowledge* of what is 'out there' – that is something which we can never know. It is, rather, a quest for an ever more accurate *model* of what is out there: for greater *verisimilitude* in our understanding of reality. Even if we cannot know exactly what is out there, we can still get closer and closer to it through refining our models of it; but absolute truth is ultimately unattainable, in the same way that, as we have seen, absolutely accurate measurement is unattainable.

(A theological writer has made a similar point in rather an amusing way, by putting in the index at the back of one of his books references to 'Truth, ultimate'. If you look up the pages indicated, you will find that they are completely blank![4])

All this leads us to an interesting philosophical question. To what extent is the information gathered by the sciences actually describing what is 'out there' at all? Is all we are doing in fact constructing models which are imposed on a reality we can never really know – do we in fact *construct*, or *invent*, scientific information in our minds rather than *discover* it in the physical world external to ourselves? The view that says that there is a reality 'out there' that we can discover through our experiments is sometimes called *realism*, whilst the alternative view, that all we ever really do in the sciences is invent interpretations of the fundamentally unknowable environment in which we find ourselves, imposing some kind of order (which has in fact no reality outside our imaginations) on the flux of events in which we find ourselves caught up, is known as *non-realism* (or, sometimes, *instrumentalism*). It must be said that out-and-out non-realism has several difficulties associated with it, most notably perhaps the observation that there is a remarkable interconnectedness about the physical world. A model that is devised to explain a particular observation may actually link in to explanations of a number of other observations as well, which a non-realist understanding of the universe might not anticipate. Most philosophers of science therefore tend more towards a form of *critical realism*, maintaining that whilst our theories are indeed human constructions, and are therefore fallible, there is nevertheless actually a reality 'out there', the operations of which we can begin to understand through our models. Such a critical realist approach fits in well with Popper's understanding of science as a quest for ever-increasing verisimilitude rather than absolute truth. We will examine the relevance of critical realism for theology in a diversion at the end of this chapter.

Returning to Karl Popper, we may note that his ideas have been widely criticized – as we might expect, given the remarkable conclusions which he drew. One particularly penetrating criticism goes like this. Either Popper is forced to abandon rationality in order to uphold his concept of science (where are the conjectures which are to be refuted by experiment supposed to come from in the first place? Either they are based on observations, in which case they have been derived by the inductive method, or else they are simply dreamt up by the scientist out of his or her imagination, in which case they are irrational); or else he is forced to admit inductive methods into his model of how science works, in order to provide a means of testing the relative value of competing theories (we have to resort to experiment to decide which of two possible explanations of something is the best one). In either case, the argument goes, Popper's theory needs to be changed.[5]

At a more subjective level, though, we don't need logical argument to see that Popper's idea of science just isn't the way that science, or scientists, work at a practical level, however theoretically satisfying Popper's idea may be felt to be. A philosopher named Imre Lakatos (who himself proposed a radical revision of Popper's ideas) once commented, 'Do you know a scientist who wants to falsify his theory?' That is of course the last thing most scientists are trying to do; and, indeed, it flies in the face of basic human psychology. If someone has devised a theory, they are surely far more likely to want to defend its accuracy than to spend their time searching out ways of proving it wrong! I certainly think that Lakatos has a point: Popper's model of the scientific enterprise just doesn't ring true in my own experience of how scientists tend to work in practice. Still, Popper's model does provide a way, the only successful way that I have come across, in which to distinguish between science and non-science. He also introduces two very helpful ideas: that of falsifiability as a means of distinguishing science from non-science, and that of a quest for verisimilitude replacing that of a quest for (unascertainable) certain knowledge, or truth.

Incidentally, it's worth just briefly noting here why Popper was so keen to devise a criterion of demarcation between science and non-science in the first place. At the time when he was writing, the theories of two men were becoming increasingly popular throughout Europe, and each of them were subsequently to affect radically the social and political life of the entire world. Each of these men claimed that their theories were scientific, but Popper was keen to maintain in both cases that they were not. Those men were the psychologist Sigmund Freud and the socio–economist Karl Marx.

Rationality

The rationality of science, we might think, is pretty well beyond reproach. The rational figure of a scientist surely stands in the popular imagination at the opposite pole to the vague figure of an imaginative artist – a poet, perhaps. However, it turns out that even the rationality of science has been questioned in recent decades. One of the most important criticisms of this aspect of science is that expounded by Thomas Kuhn in his highly influential book *The Structure of Scientific Revolutions*. He distinguishes between 'normal science', or science as it is practised by most scientists for most of the time, and 'scientific revolutions', which take place when the ideas underlying scientific practices are challenged and changed. Let's look at this distinction a little more closely.

About normal science, Kuhn writes: 'Normal science does not aim at novelties of fact or theory and, when successful, finds none.'[6] Normal science is content with making observations and deductions in accordance with the world-view (Kuhn uses the word *paradigm*) adhered to by contemporary scientists. This paradigm is basically the whole mass of ideas, theories, interpretations, and so on which form the background to the scientist's outlook. It shapes the way in which scientists view the universe, and as a result it inevitably guides the way in which they construct their experiments, make their observations, and interpret their findings. A 'scientific revolution', on the other hand, changes everything. It is characterized by the way in which it proceeds. As more and more 'normal science' is done, it is found that inconsistencies and inadequacies begin to emerge in the old paradigm. An expected result doesn't materialize: a reaction that should, according to theory, give one result in fact gives a different one. These inconsistencies gradually lead to a crisis situation, during which many new theories, explaining the new data, jostle with each other for acceptance. Eventually, one particular theory emerges which, by a general consensus of opinion among practising scientists, is best able to re-define the paradigm within which science operates: a 'paradigm shift' occurs to this new viewpoint; and normal science begins again, within this new paradigm.

Kuhn has stressed that during a 'crisis' period the rules governing the way in which normal science operates are suspended. He has written, 'Paradigm choice can never be unequivocally settled by logic and experiment alone'.[7] In other words, during a 'crisis' period, science itself may actually be said to proceed at other than a purely rational, intellectual level. The choice of a new paradigm can be influenced by all sorts of things: aesthetic taste, ideological stance, intuition, and so on. A *non-rational* component is therefore introduced into the progress of science.

Kuhn, as we might expect, has not been without his critics either. Some have suggested that his model of scientific change is rather over-dramatic a way of looking at things. Sometimes, perhaps, substantial paradigm shifts occur, reflecting changes in our understanding of certain phenomena, but *really* major changes of the type which Kuhn describes take place only very rarely. The two most often discussed examples of this type of change are the Copernican revolution – this was the change in viewpoint that led to it being generally accepted that the Earth goes around the sun, rather than vice versa – and the much discussed and endlessly fascinating theories of quantum physics, which have replaced those of classical (Newtonian) physics, at least when we try to account for the behaviour of very small systems.

A different example shows very clearly the way in which Kuhn's model for science allows for the operation of a *counter-intuitive* element in science, which a hardline rationalist like Popper would seem to wish to get rid of entirely. (By 'counter-intuitive' I mean an explanation of something that is contrary to what might be our automatic expectations.) These days, we know that when things burn they combine with oxygen in the air. However, before the discovery of oxygen, there were rather different theories about what happened when things burned. Probably the most popular theory accounting for the phenomenon of combustion was the so-called *phlogiston* theory. It was observed that some materials burned violently (magnesium, for example), some burned steadily (wood, for example), and some did not burn at all (gold, for example). Moreover, it was observed that when substances burned, the residue – ash – was usually a dull powder which, when weighed, was greater in mass than the material burned. Phlogiston was a hypothetical substance whose existence satisfactorily explained all these observations. Materials which burned contained this substance, which was given up as they burned in the form of a flame. It had negative mass, so that a substance which lost phlogiston gained in weight. The more violent the combustion (so the reasoning went), the more phlogiston the substance contained.

Such an idea now may strike us as pretty daft. But if all you have to go on is what you observe with your eyes, the idea that in combustion materials actually *combine* with a gas in the air is not at all obvious. In this case, what turns out to be the 'correct' solution of the problem of how things burn is the counter-intuitive one: the one that actually goes against what is apparently obvious. Similarly, simple observations may tell us that the sun goes around the earth: that the opposite is, in fact, the case is also a counter-intuitive assertion. With Kuhn's model of how science operates, we can see in both these cases paradigm shifts occurring. Scientists abandon one way of thinking, however persuasive it may once have seemed, in favour of an alternative that better explains later observations, even though it may require considerable imaginative insight to perceive that alternative. It is hard to see how Popper's theories of scientific development could cater for the proposal of theories of this type, radically and imaginatively revising the whole way in which things are seen.

Not only in the way in which we form theories, but also in the way in which we select the theory which is best able to explain our observations, non-rational processes may have a part to play. (I deliberately use the expression 'non-rational' rather than 'irrational', since the word 'irrational' has all sorts of connotations I wouldn't wish to impute to the scientists concerned with a theory choice such as we are discussing.) Let us return for a moment to thinking about our generalized theory, T_1, which I mentioned earlier. The observations which we have made may in fact be explained by a number of different theories. What makes our theory T_1 better than someone else's alternative theory, which likewise explains all the facts at our disposal?

For example, consider the photoelectric effect. This is the name given to the observation that when light of a frequency above a certain critical value shines on a metal surface, that surface gives off electrons. The photoelectric effect may be explained by the theory that light striking a metal surface consists of particles which give up the energy they possess to electrons in the metal surface, causing their ejection from it. What about the alternative theory that in fact there are tiny, invisible, undetectable fairies which sleep on metal surfaces, but which are woken up by light; and, when they are awoken, these fairies dance around and kick electrons out of the metal? This may sound daft; but by what criteria should we reject it? Why do we choose one theory over another? What is it that makes one theory better than another?

Several criteria have been given for deciding between competing theories. Three such criteria are that the better theory is the *simpler* one, the one with greater *predicting power*, and the one which is most *consistent* with other theories. The reasons for preferring consistency and greater predicting power are obvious, and are, of course, largely practical. A theory which agrees with other ones, and which enables you to make lots of predictions about how other systems, related to the one under consideration, will behave, is better than one which is at odds with other theories relating to the system under investigation, and which explains the particular system you're looking at but is totally irrelevant to any other situation. The preference for a simple theory over a more complex one goes back to the medieval philosophical principle known as Occam's razor: this states that ideas should not be multiplied beyond necessity. In other words, where a simple explanation is possible, it is to be preferred to a more complicated one. The fairies on the metal surface being an added idea, complicating matters, we would tend to prefer the theory that didn't require their presence. This may strike you as rather obvious; but note that this is an aesthetic judgement, rather than a rational one. Here again, we may see non-rational processes coming into play in our analysis of a scientific situation.

Objectivity

Tied in with this issue of rationality is the issue of our fourth alleged characteristic of science, that it is *objective*. An author who has written very carefully and very perceptively about the role played by the observer in an experiment is Michael Polanyi, himself a physical scientist (unlike most of the other philosophers discussed here). He noted the important part played by the interpretive *skill* of the experimenter in finding or selecting observations in the first place. This is how he put it: 'Making sense of experience is a skilful act, which impresses the personal participation of the scientist on the resulting knowledge.'[8] There is, it appears, a *subjective* element in the gathering of scientific information.

This point is most clearly to be seen in experimental quantum physics. Quantum physics is a special type of physics which comes most evidently into play when we consider very small (atomic and sub-atomic) systems. It was developed early in this century when advances in the accuracy of our measuring apparatus made very small physical systems accessible to study, and it immediately became clear that the kind of physics developed in the last century no longer accounted for the observations of small systems that could then be made.

The vital role played by the observer in the way in which he or she relates to the outcome of an event in quantum physics has been expressed in the famous paradox of 'Schrödinger's cat'. Erwin Schrödinger was an early quantum physicist, responsible for the equation bearing his name that is the starting-point of wave mechanics; and the remarkable story of his apocryphal cat illustrates the importance of the observer in the context of the world of quantum physics. The paradox runs something like this. There are some systems which can exist in two different states: for example, an electron can possess 'up' or 'down' spin. Which state a particular electron has is not in fact determined *until you look at it*. In other words, until the observer looks to see which state the electron is in, it is (potentially, at least) in both states: only when it is observed does it 'decide' to be in one particular state. Similarly, a particle which may or may not decay within a certain period of time, until it is examined is in fact in a state of 'having decayed' and 'having not decayed' simultaneously, from the observer's point of view. So what?, you may think. However, now imagine a system containing such a particle as this linked to an apparatus which contains a deadly poison. If the particle decays, the apparatus releases the poison: if it doesn't decay, the poison is not released. This apparatus is placed inside a sealed box, along with an unfortunate cat. At the end of an interval of time after which there is an equal chance of the particle having decayed or not having decayed, then, until it is observed, from the observer's point of view it has in fact both decayed and not decayed with equal probability: the poison has and has not been released; and the cat is both alive and dead. From the cat's point of view, however, it can hardly be both alive *and* dead simultaneously – it must, obviously, be either one or the other! The point of this paradox is that it illustrates the way in which the facts of quantum physics are utterly beyond the boundaries of our normal experience, revealing a world totally different to that which we are used to: they may be seen as such by this attempt to scale them up to our more familiar, observable world. This paradox also illustrates the way in which the observer and the thing observed are bound up together in an experiment in the quantum world. This runs counter to all the assumptions of classical, nineteenth-century physics, in which it was taken for granted that the person doing the experiment stood totally outside it, observing a system completely without affecting what was going on in it.

It would appear, then, that we are moving towards the idea that observations and theories are not the *objective* and *rational* things they are sometimes made out to be. Rather, there are frequently *subjective* and *non-rational* components to them. Many examples from the history of science confirm this. For example, consider the story of the discovery of the structure of benzene. Benzene was for many years a well-known compound, derived from coal tar and used widely in organic chemistry. It was known to have the formula C_6H_6. However, its molecular structure remained problematic. Simple compounds of hydrogen and carbon in which the ratio of hydrogen to carbon is 2:1 or less tend to be pretty reactive towards many reagents (hydrogen and chlorine, for example), as they contain carbon–carbon double bonds: so this formula suggests that benzene should be very reactive. However, it is in fact far less reactive than this formula would lead us to expect. Many chemists tried unsuccessfully to suggest ideas for the structure of benzene. A man named Kekulé then made the suggestion that in the benezene molecule the carbon atoms it contains are joined to each other in a ring formation: other chemists had always assumed that they were joined in a long chain. This simple suggestion correctly solved a long-standing problem in organic chemistry. Yet it was not reasoned out logically by Kekulé: rather, he thought of it spontaneously during a day-dream, in which he saw carbon-chains like snakes, one of which seized its own tail. Kekulé's remarkable conclusion from this episode was: 'Let us learn to dream, and then perhaps we shall learn the truth.'[9]

Reductionism

We now come to the fifth of our characteristics of science, that it is *reductionistic*. You'll remember that this is the idea that the explanations of the behaviour of things are always to be found in the behaviour of their component parts. In addressing this characteristic, I'd like to introduce the thought of another philosopher, named Paul Feyerabend. He is something of an extremist, who maintains that *everything* in science – observations, theories, the lot – is completely relative, subjective and non-rational. Like Kuhn, Feyerabend adopts an historical approach to the philosophy of science; and, again like Kuhn, he dismisses the idea that science always proceeds logically and rationally. He maintains that science, as it is generally understood, is limited in its scope and should not be looked upon as the sole generator and arbiter of truth. He writes, '[Scientists] insinuate that their standards are *essential* for arriving at the Truth, or for getting Results . . . [but] science is only one of the many instruments people invented to cope with their surroundings. It is not the only one, it is not infallible, and it has become too powerful.'[10]

In choosing a scientific outlook on life over any other, says Feyerabend, the chooser is necessarily making a non-rational choice. This observation is analogous to that made by Kuhn when considering theory selection. Feyerabend maintains in addition that a purely scientific world-view is inadequate in catering for most people's needs: 'There are many ways of being in the world . . . people have a right to use the ways that appeal to them . . . using these ways they may lead a happy and fulfilling life.'[11] 'Scientific results and the scientific ethos (if there is such a thing) are simply too thin a foundation for a life worth living. Many scientists agree with this judgement.'[12] Feyerabend has summarized his own so-called 'anarchistic' position thus: 'There is only *one* principle that can be defended under *all* circumstances and in *all* stages of human development. It is the principle: *anything goes.*'[13] You see what I mean about Feyerabend being something of an extremist!

Feyerabend's thought, however extreme it may seem, is important because it embraces a more *holistic* vision of science than is normal. This is by no means a bad thing. In fact, there is currently discernible a more general questioning of the usual reductionist approach of science going on. James Lovelock's controversial Gaia hypothesis – the theory that our planet is a single, self-regulating system – is perhaps the best-known recent example of holistic thinking,[14] although in fact scientists from right across the scientific spectrum, from physicists to physiologists, have been contributing to this trend.

A fascinating experiment from the world of quantum physics has shown the relatedness of entities in the physical world. It was carried out by Alain Aspect and his collaborators in response to an apparent paradox in quantum theory that had been pointed out by Einstein and his fellow-workers. It transpires that particles which possess a property that may have one of two values – 'up' and 'down' spin, for example – may be produced under certain circumstances in pairs, with one particle possessing 'up' spin and the other 'down' spin. As with the particle in the Schrödinger's cat paradox, until one or other particle has this property measured, both particles possess both 'up' and 'down' spin. However, once the spin of one particle is measured (and found, say, to be 'up') then it transpires that the other particle 'knows' *instantaneously* that it has to be 'down'. This result – obtained by Aspect in a study of photons – shows that at the quantum level, systems that have been at some point in time in contact with each other retain a 'memory' of that contact, even when they are later separated. As Polkinghorne puts it:

Whatever the microscopic world is, it cannot be a collection of local, separated parts. The paradox of subatomic physics is that it cannot be treated atomistically. This peculiarity of quantum theory is intrinsic and is not an artefact of some incomplete or hamfisted way of setting up the theory (as Einstein had hoped).[15]

Rather than treat an entity in isolation, as the reductionist programme seeks to do in studying its make-up and behaviour, it appears that at the quantum level the relationships between entities need to be considered too. Once again, the necessity of an holistic vision is indicated: the effects discussed here cannot be explained by considering entities by themselves, but only in connection with one another, and with their past behaviour. The behaviour of Aspect's photons is only explicable in terms of the total system which produced each of them.

Another term I should like to introduce at this point is *antireductionism*. This is the view that it is appropriate to think of some things in terms of the *emergence* of higher-order behaviour from matter in non-reducible ways. The non-localized order in quantum-level systems shown by the Aspect experiment is an example of this, and others have been suggested. This is a fascinating topic, to which we shall return at the end of this chapter.

First, though, let us bring to a conclusion this consideration of the meanings of the words 'belief' and 'knowledge'. We have seen that the understanding of science as an activity that generates knowledge, an activity characterized by its rationality, its objectivity, its use of the inductive method, and its espousal of a reductionist philosophy, has been radically challenged. There are things which, science has shown us, are unknowable for practical reasons, and there are things which are fundamentally unknowable. (This extends even to the discipline of mathematics, in which Gödel's theorem indicates that there exist mathematical statements which are incapable of being proved.)[16]

Moreover, the kind of knowledge that science itself generates for us has been shown to be provisional, rather than established for all time. Not only this, but we have also seen that the knowledge generated by scientific practice has a subjective component – it is to some extent inevitably dependent upon the person of the individual who records it; and scientific information may, moreover, be influenced by non-rational factors, both in the way in which it is obtained, and in its subsequent analysis.

Theological perspectives

Theological theories, ideas and concepts are surely very similar in kind to the theories, ideas and concepts of science thus understood. Let's go through those five characteristics of the nineteenth-century understanding of science again, comparing them with a few theological perspectives on these issues.

1. *Determinism.* Christianity has always upheld the free will of individuals, insisting that not all our responses are determined in every detail by the circumstances in which they are made, and that making responsible choices is a vital part of being human. Our response to God is considered to be one such choice. The fact that science demonstrates that we inhabit a universe which is not fully deterministic restores a significance to this understanding which a rigidly deterministic outlook could be held to undermine, and makes the views of science and theology appear less radically opposed on this issue than we might have expected.

2. *Induction/deduction.* Popper's conclusion that science deals only with things that are falsifiable, and that scientific ideas are therefore necessarily incomplete, bears interesting comparison with theology, which in the same way deals with a subject matter (God) about which our ideas can only ever be partial. Indeed, this philosophical approach to the sciences bears a certain resemblance to the so-called *via negativa*, the approach of what is known as apophatic theology, which states that we can only make meaningful assertions about what God *is not*, rather than about what he *is*. And, just as scientific theories continually change, so theological theories can change, too – indeed, I would contend, they *must* do so for theology to be a living, dynamic discipline.

3. *Rationality.* Although science is by and large a rational activity, we have seen that it may proceed in non-rational ways. There is frequently an element of both rational and non-rational processes involved in the overall progress of science. Religious experiences may be non-rational from any point of view other than that of the one who experiences them (and even, perhaps, from the point of view of that person, too); but they may at least be discussed and analysed in a rational way. It might also be urged that the very rationality of those aspects of the universe which we are able to observe may be the cause of quasi-'religious' feelings of awe and wonder. I would urge, therefore, that rational and non-rational factors are bound up together, and may both have a part to play, in the sciences and in theology. Theology

is fundamentally a rational pursuit, even though, like science, both rational and non-rational processes may be involved in its progress.

4. *Objectivity/subjectivity.* We have seen that scientific procedures may have subjective as well as objective components to them. Ideas about God also have a subjective component to them. Everyone who experiences God, in whatever way, has a slightly different story to tell of that experience, and the record of human encounters with the divine found in the Bible is similarly varied. The theologian is therefore constantly drawing on subjective reports concerning his or her subject matter. But there are objective components to theology, too – components, that is, which stand outside the person of the believer, and are generally available for inspection. Sacred texts, creeds, and the like may all be analysed in an objective fashion. (Whether or not God himself comes into this category – whether or not God himself has an objective reality independent of the individual who believes in him – has been hotly debated. We will look at this issue in one of the diversions at the end of this chapter.) In other words, in practice both science and theology use a combination of subjective experience and objective analysis.

5. *Reductionism/holism.* Reductionist ideas fit in well with the assumption that there is no God: they may even be used to justify the assumption that there is no God; but antireductionist ideas, whilst of course in no way proving God's existence, do at least allow more readily for the possibility of it. Theologians who speak of the cosmos as in some sense the creation of God may make reference to its inter-connectedness, witnessed to also by the biblical statement that 'God saw everything that he had made, and indeed, it was very good' (Genesis 1. 31).[17] This may be tied in to recent holistic thinking about the universe we inhabit.

Summary

Let us now summarize the argument of this chapter so far. Instead of thinking of knowledge and belief as utterly different things, it surely makes more sense to think of them as occupying positions towards the ends of a continuous scale. Science tends to yield us information that is nearer to the 'knowledge' end of the scale, and theology tends to yield us information that is nearer to the 'belief' end of the scale, but in fact there are elements of knowledge in theological statements and elements of belief in scientific statements. Both knowledge and belief are inevitably involved all the time in all human inquiries. Scientists are to a certain extent necessarily 'believers', and believers are to some extent necessarily 'scientists', in that there is a 'knowledge' component to the faith they profess. The Swiss psychologist C. G. Jung was once asked in an interview if he believed in God; and, famously, he replied, 'I don't believe – I know.' The blurring of the conventional distinction between belief and knowledge implied by this statement is, I would suggest, only right and proper.

Before moving on, I'd like to expand a little on two fascinating topics which we have touched on in the course of this chapter: first, the debate between realist and non-realist understandings of God and of the world; and second, the concept of antireductionism, and its significance for theology.

Diversion 1: realism and non-realism

As mentioned above, both realist and non-realist views of science have been held by scientists, although most philosophers of science now tend towards a form of critical realism. In a striking parallel, the argument over realist and non-realist interpretations of God has also raged in the field of theology. In the same way that we are faced with these two ways of interpreting our theories about the physical world – as describing things which are really 'out there', or as being things which are simply constructions of our minds – so, in approaching the subject of God, we are faced with the same problem. What exactly are we describing when we talk about God? Is God something (or someone) who really exists 'out there', or is he, rather, something we have invented in order to make sense of the physical, mental and spiritual environment in which we find ourselves?

Critics of religious belief frequently assert the latter to be the case. Atheists have for centuries maintained that God is no more than a human invention. Debate on the issue has raged amongst theologians too, some of whom argue in favour of non-realist views, and urge that our understanding of the nature of God needs to be changed in the light of those views. In recent years, such a non-realist position has been powerfully put forward by Don Cupitt, who has written: 'The true God is not God as picturesque supernatural fact, but God as our religious idea.'[18] The espousal of views of this kind by Anthony Freeman, who, like Cupitt, is an Anglican clergyman, led to his widely publicized dismissal by his bishop in a blaze of ill-informed media comment. From the confessional tone of Freeman's book, however, it would appear that he personally finds there to be no inconsistency in his holding these views whilst working as a Christian minister. Rejecting the idea of a supernatural God, yet wishing still to affirm his belief in God, he writes: 'I have decided to change my use of the word God. Instead of referring it to a supernatural being, I shall apply it to the sum of all my values and ideals in life.'[19] This shifting of the theological goalposts is ingenious, but is it really absolutely necessary?

We saw earlier that many philosophers of science now opt for a form of 'critical realism', in which the reality of a natural world 'out there' is recognized whilst the knowledge which we have of it is acknowledged to be both provisional and fallible. In the same way, critical realism as an approach to understanding the nature of God is increasingly being explored by theologians. Tom Wright, a New Testament scholar, advocates such an understanding as being highly appropriate to theological study. He has written of it:

> This path leads to critical reflection on the products of our enquiry into 'reality', so that our assertions about 'reality' acknowledge their own provisionality. Knowledge, in other words, although in principle concerning realities independent of the knower, is never itself independent of the knower.[20]

Wright would affirm that theology *is* the study of an objective reality that we call God, even though the statements that we are able to make about God are necessarily only provisional.

In this approval of critical realism, by many theologians and scientists, as the best way in which to think about the theories put forward by their disciplines, we have a clear coming-together of the two disciplines, as each seeks to understand the way in which its theories relate to the external reality which is the object of its study.

Diversion 2: antireductionism

The whole area of antireductionist thinking is so wide-ranging and so fascinating, and its theological implications are so profound, that in many respects it warrants a book in its own right. The interested reader is strongly urged to pursue this issue further than the confines of this book permit me to do here.[21]

It is also a very complex area. We should note to begin with that several different kinds of reductionist thinking have been identified. For example, a distinction has been made[22] between *methodological reductionism* (the idea that the way in which scientific experiments are carried out involves breaking complex entities down into their component parts), *ontological reductionism* (the idea that complex entities actually *are* 'nothing but' the parts of which they are comprised), and *epistemological reductionism* (the idea that the theories of, say, biology, are ultimately explicable in terms of the theories of physics). The first of these is a purely practical convenience: most scientists are probably reductionist in this sense. The second and third are more complex, and more hotly debated. I believe that it makes sense to talk about complex entities in terms that imply they are *not* 'nothing but' the sum of their parts, and I would suggest that this does validate our talking *as if* some new entity were present, even though this is not in fact the case in any physical sense. However, I would not wish to espouse a full-blooded ontological antireductionism. Of greater significance, I think, is the fact that in practice we are obliged to use language in non-reducible ways to talk about emergent qualities of matter, so that our theories are not always reducible to those of physics and chemistry (where highly complex entities arise, other considerations need also to be taken into account). In the discussions which follow, I shall therefore be thinking primarily in terms of epistemological antireductionism.

Antireductionist thinking, we have seen, maintains that not all that we observe in nature is explicable purely in terms of the behaviour of things being dictated by the behaviour of the parts of which they are comprised. Rather, it suggests that some phenomena are best explained in terms of the *emergence* of higher-order behaviour in large systems in ways that are not reducible to the behaviour of their components. This idea of emergence may be exemplified using three different systems in which emergent properties have been said to arise: water, a cell, and a human brain. A water molecule is not wet; yet many of them together display the property of 'wetness'. A simple combination of proteins, nucleic acids, lipids and a few other chemicals is not alive; but a cell is. A neuron in the human brain is not conscious; but acting together with other neurons it produces the phenomenon which we call 'consciousness'. Wetness, life and consciousness have all been described as emergent properties of their respective systems: they may not be fully described in terms of the 'bits' of which the systems in which they arise are made. We may define an emergent reality as a fundamentally irreducible concept referring to a feature or function or activity in the world around us, which arises from some arrangement of physical matter, and which cannot be attributed to the components of that matter, nor explained solely in terms of their individual physical behaviour.

To generalize, we might say that the phenomenon of antireductionism yields two interesting results. *First*, parts generate wholes, which may be complex entities that are not fully characterizable simply as the sum of their parts; and *second*, wholes influence parts – once an organized, complex entity has come about, it may influence the behaviour of smaller entities which comprise it, or which interact with it. This second phenomenon is sometimes referred to as 'downward causation' or 'top-down causation'.

How does all this impinge on theology? I would suggest that there are four important areas where the antireductionist approach to science, and the concept of emergent reality which I have discussed above, may be seen to be of theological significance. The first of these is simply that, whilst reductionist views of the universe are very difficult (although perhaps not impossible) to reconcile with the existence of a God who created, sustains and loves that universe, and are impossible to reconcile with the idea of a God who is able to enter into personal relationships with the created order, antireductionist views, whilst they do not, of course, prove the existence of God, at least allow for the possibility of his existence.

Second, the idea of emergent reality brings back a fundamental unpredictability into our picture of nature, like many other ideas developed by physicists this century (such as quantum theory and chaos theory, as mentioned above), since an emergent quality is not necessarily predictable in advance from any analysis of the parts of the entity whence that quality emerges. Nature is never, finally, completely understandable and totally predictable. Through the ordering of its parts it produces complex wholes in ways that could not have been predicted in advance, and with properties that could not necessarily be deduced from the properties of the parts – even if they are understandable in retrospect. In other words, nature is mysterious; and if this fact is accepted and recognized, then the credibility of the discipline of theology, in which Mystery has a very important part to play, must surely be enhanced as a consequence.

Third, the concept of emergent reality provides a potentially highly useful source of metaphors, models and analogies which can be used by theologians. The idea that a phenomenon may be present in, and yet more than, its component parts might be said to lend support, by analogy, to what are known as *panentheistic* views (the idea behind panentheism being that God is present throughout, yet not fully contained by, the universe). Such views have been developed by several Christian writers in the last decade or so. For example, in the same way that Lovelock's Gaia hypothesis treats the Earth as a single organism, it has been suggested that the universe might be similarly treated, and viewed in some figurative sense as the body of God. The reality of God may then be regarded as an emergent quality of the universe.[23]

In addition, the concept of top-down causation also lends itself to borrowing by theologians. In particular, it has led to some interesting speculation regarding the vexed issue of how God can interact with the world. Christian theology frequently makes mention of the possibility of God acting in the world, either through the lives of individuals or through intervening in some way in the physical order in order to produce 'miracles'.

It is often assumed that this would require God to act in some way within the causal complex of physical events, possibly by disrupting in some way the chains of cause-and-effect that we see in the physical world. It must be said that many people feel considerable unease with the idea of a God who behaves in such an apparently haphazard and capricious way. In response to this unease, Peacocke has supplied an analogy for God's action in the world which avoids this idea of an interventionist God. He suggests that the way in which we are conscious of being selves acting upon our bodies gives us a model for the way in which God interacts with the physical universe:

> In my actions I am a transcendent causal agent expressing myself in and through the physical structure of my body. Can we not similarly conceive of God as agent in the world? God's transcendence over the world in which he is immanent implies that he expresses his intentions within the causal nexus of the natural world.[24]

Elsewhere, Peacocke writes of this idea: 'In this model, God would be regarded as exerting continuously top-down causative influences on the world-as-a-whole in a way analogous to that whereby we in our thinking can exert effects on our bodies in a "top-down" manner.'[25] This model provides a fascinating way of thinking about an issue that has often been contentious, both within the Church and between it and those outside it.

The fourth area in which antireductionist views might provide insights of theological significance is that of the mind–body problem. This is the problem of the relationship between the mind and the body of human beings: between physical and mental phenomena: between the complex lump of organic matter that constitutes your brain and the 'you' who is a conscious being, reading this book. This issue is of course crucial in thinking about what actually constitutes human beings: what the 'I' means in the statements 'I believe' and 'I know'. We shall consider this question further in the next chapter.

NOTES

1. This example is taken from Arthur Peacocke's book, *Theology for a Scientific Age* (enlarged edition, SCM Press, 1993), p. 49, a magisterial work which I thoroughly recommend.
2. On chaos theory, see James Gleick's *Chaos* (Penguin Books, 1988), a very readable introduction to this subject.

   Here's an example of how a deterministic equation can generate unpredictability, for those of you with a good head for mathematics (if you don't fall into this category, then please feel free to ignore this note!). This example is taken from Gleick's book. Consider the equation $x^4 - 1 = 0$. This is an equation with two obvious solutions: $x = +1$ and $x = -1$. It also has two complex solutions, $x = +i$ and $x = -i$, where i is the square root of -1. If these four solutions are plotted on an Argand diagram (a kind of graph, with 'real' numbers on the horizontal axis and 'imaginary' numbers – numbers that are multiples of i – on the vertical axis), they mark out a square, with its corners sited on the two axes. One might expect that if one were to use an iterative process to reach a solution – making a guess at a solution, feeding that into the equation, arriving at a better guess, feeding that in, and so on until a solution is reached – then points (guesses) on the Argand diagram would move towards the nearest solution in a straightforward, predictable way. In fact, great complexity is obtained in attempting to plot which solution a point on the Argand diagram tends towards, particularly near to the axes perpendicularly bisecting the sides of the square (i.e. along the lines $y = x$ and $y = -x$). A simple equation like this, then can yield a pattern of dazzling and apparently unpredictable complexity when analysed in detail. See Gleick's *Chaos*, pp. 217 ff., and the picture following p. 114.

3. Books by Popper include *Conjectures and Refutations* (Routledge and Kegan Paul, 4th edition, 1972) and *The Logic of Scientific Discovery* (Hutchinson, revised edition, 1980), which is probably his best-known work. A concise and well-written account of his philosophy can be found in Bryan Magee, *Popper* (Fontana, 1982).

4. This occurs in E. P. Sanders' book *Paul and Palestinian Judaism* (SCM Press, 1977).

5. This argument is developed by W. H. Newton-Smith in his book *The Rationality of Science* (Routledge and Kegan Paul, 1981). This book contains interesting critical accounts of the writings not only of Popper but also of the other writers discussed in this section (with the exception of Polanyi).

6. T. S. Kuhn, *The Structure of Scientific Revolutions* (University of Chicago Press, 2nd edition, 1970), p. 52.

7. Ibid., p. 54.

8. Michael Polanyi, *Personal Knowledge* (Routledge and Kegan Paul, 1958), p. 60.

9. Quoted in R. T. Morrison and R. N. Boyd, *Organic Chemistry* (Allyn and Bacon Inc., 3rd edition, 1973), p. 319.

10. Paul Feyerabend, *Against Method* (Verso, revised edition, 1988), p. 166.

11. Paul Feyerabend, *Farewell to Reason* (Verso, 1987), p. 62.

12. Feyerabend, *Against Method*, p. 135.

13. Feyerabend, *Against Method*, p. 19 (and see also *Farewell to Reason*, p. 36).
    Is it possible to be a liberal fundamentalist? If so, Feyerabend must be one to whom such a label could be applied. Certainly he refuses to tolerate views apart from his own relativistic one, and he lampoons his opponents mercilessly. The following is typical: 'From the very beginning "critical" philosophers define human relations in their own intellectualised way. Congratulating themselves on their tolerance they are either ignorant, or dishonest, or (my own conjecture) both.' (*Farewell to Reason*, p. 85).

14. For more about Lovelock's Gaia hypothesis, see *The Ages of Gaia* (Oxford University Press, 1988).

15. John Polkinghorne, *Reason and Reality* (SPCK, 1991), p. 95. This is a very good read, as is Polkinghorne's earlier trilogy of books, *One World*, *Science and Creation* and *Science and Providence*, and his more recent *Science and Christian Belief* (all SPCK). Many of his arguments are summed up in his most recent work, unforgettably titled *Quarks, Chaos and Christianity* (Triangle, 1994).

16. For more on Gödel's theorem, see Douglas R. Hofstadter, *Gödel, Escher, Bach* (Penguin, 1980), especially pp. 17 ff.

17. All biblical quotations in this book are taken from the New Revised Standard Version (NRSV), with the exception of quotations from the Psalms, which are taken from the liturgical psalter of the Alternative Service Book.

18. Don Cupitt, *The Sea of Faith* (BBC Publications, 1984), p. 270.

19. Anthony Freeman, *God in Us* (SCM Press, 1993), p. 25.

20. N. T. Wright, *The New Testament and the People of God* (SPCK, 1992), p. 35.

21. The reader might like to begin with the references contained in my article 'Antireductionism and Theology', published in *Theology*, xcvii (1994), pp. 433 ff., from which the argument presented here is condensed.

22. See A. Peacocke, *God and the New Biology* (Dent, 1986), chapter 1.

23. See, for example, Grace Jantzen's book *God's World, God's Body* (Darton Longman and Todd, 1984) and Sallie McFague's *The Body of God* (SCM Press, 1993). This is undoubtedly an intriguing idea, even if it is not in some respects a wholly satisfactory one. For example, it is predicted that the universe we inhabit will, at some point in the future, end, either through the galaxies it contains – which are currently flying apart from one another – being pulled back together through the forces of attraction between them, resulting in a so-called 'big crunch', or else in a state where all energy in the universe is equally distributed and no further work may be done in it (the so-called 'heat death' of the universe). If the universe is indeed the body of God, even in a purely metaphorical sense, then the metaphor needs to encompass the idea of God's death. This is not an idea which many theologians have been willing to countenance, since it flies directly in the face of many traditional understandings of God – for example, of God as one who exists outside time, and certainly outside mortality.

24. A. Peacocke, *Intimations of Reality* (University of Notre Dame Press, 1984), p. 75.

25. A. Peacocke, *Theology for a Scientific Age*, p. 161.

3

The believer/knower

Twice two is four is, in my opinion, nothing but impudence.
Fyodor Dostoevsky, *Notes from Underground*

What do we mean by 'I'?

This is perhaps the most basic question of all. What is a human being? Who am I? All the talk in the last chapter about knowing and believing assumes that there are people of some sort who can believe and know in the first place. Science and religion sometimes appear to put forward rather different models of what a person actually is. Let's now have a look at those views, and see whether they are wholly incompatible or not.

The materialist view

Scientific understandings of what a human being is have, as is right and proper, focused on the bits of a human being that can be looked at and examined: that is to say, on the physical matter that makes up our bodies. These scientific understandings are necessarily materialistic, and, in the past, they have tended to be reductionist in outlook.

We've already looked at reductionism. The reductionist view in the present context is neatly expressed in the outlook of the Helmholz school of medicine, which flourished in Germany in the mid-nineteenth century. One member of that school, named Du Bois, gave classic expression to this position, writing the following:

I pledged a solemn oath to put into effect this truth: 'No other forces than the common physical–chemical ones are active within the organism. In those cases which cannot at the time be explained by these forces one has either to find the specific way or form of their action by means of the physical–mathematical method or to assume new forces equal in dignity to the chemical–physical forces inherent in matter, reducible to the force of attraction and repulsion.'[1]

This sort of thorough-going reductionist approach to what constitutes human beings seems to me to represent an assumption that is still common in many peoples' thinking about what human beings are. It is the sort of view which Dostoevsky violently opposes in his *Notes from Underground*, from which the quotation heading this chapter is taken: it is the view which, when taken to extremes, states that all the operations of human beings, all their thoughts and actions, may ultimately be reduced to sequences of events which are governed by mathematical formulae.

In spite of the forcefully stated opposition of Dostoevsky and other critics, however, it cannot be denied that the materialist approach towards trying to understand what it is that makes human beings tick is in many ways a very satisfying one. It certainly works in the treatment of many diseases, for example when the disease in question is due to a chemical imbalance of some sort in the body. In such cases, treatment is provided by giving further chemicals – drugs of some sort or another – to the sufferer, and these modify his or her body chemistry in such a way as to counteract the effect of the disease. As an example of this procedure, consider the treatment of diabetes. This is a condition in which the body's glands fail to produce sufficient quantities of a chemical called insulin, which is important in the part it plays in the body – metabolizing glucoses (sugars). Concentrations of sugars therefore build up in the body, with harmful or possibly even fatal results. However, if insulin from another source is given to a person suffering from diabetes in order to make good the deficiency in the patient's body, then it enables the reactions metabolizing glucose to proceed as they would normally do, and the disease is kept under control. Here we have a classic example of a condition caused by a simple chemical deficiency, and put right by making up that deficiency. In the same way, some diseases are caused by an excess of a chemical in the body, and may be treated by the removal of that excess. (Of course, many of the diseases that affect the incredibly complicated machinery of our bodies are not as straightforward as this, in terms of either their causes or their cures.)

This materialist view of the nature of human beings, which I shall call reductionistic materialism, also points towards a solution of an age-old philosophical debate. Are people simply complex machines, or are we dual entities – do we have souls, or spirits? A reductionistic materialist would say, No: we are no more than physical entities and processes. There cannot possibly be any such thing as a soul. Such a position stands in stark contrast to what is probably the most widely held alternative to it: that of *dualism* in our understanding of what human beings are. Put simply, the dualist position is that human beings do actually consist of two distinct things, souls and bodies. We have physical bodies which are like houses, inside which dwell our non-physical souls.

This can also be a very satisfying way in which to think about ourselves. We often feel as though we have a part of ourselves that is distinct from our bodies, and that is not subject to the same constraints that our bodies are. More or less dualistic views are of course held, explicitly or implicitly, by many religions; and, in the past, scientific–materialist views like the ones discussed above have been in marked opposition to them. There are two classic types of response which have been made to this perceived opposition between religious and scientific thinking.

The first response is to attempt to put dualist understandings of human beings on to a scientific basis. For example, recent accounts of near-death experiences (NDEs) have received a great deal of attention by both serious researchers and more speculative semi-scientists. They are sometimes cited as indicating that people can have experiences 'outside' their bodies, and hence as support for a dualistic understanding of human beings. Briefly, NDEs have occurred when people have 'died' as a result of serious injury or during the course of surgical operations: needless to say, they have subsequently been brought 'back to life', and have been able to tell of their experiences when they were, from a clinical point of view, dead. These experiences frequently involve the person concerned 'seeing' his or her body from a position outside it, feelings of peacefulness, and perceptions of bright lights. Occasionally, people are seen, and they may be identified as God, or as Jesus. There is often a sense of reluctance to 'go back' to a life in the world.

Of course, not all people who have 'died' and been revived have had these experiences: some recall nothing at all of their ordeal. The precise status of these NDEs must remain unclear: the parallels between the accounts of different people are undoubtedly fascinating, but I don't think that too much should be read into them as scientific evidence of there being a life after death, as has sometimes been claimed – at least, not until they are rather better understood than they are at present.[2]

In addition, in past years attempts have been made to demonstrate the validity of dualistic thinking by proving by physical means that souls exist within our bodies. The story has been told of one doctor a couple of centuries ago who attempted to demonstrate the truth of this hypothesis in a dramatic and compelling way. Working in a hospital, where the death of patients occurred fairly frequently, he set up a large balance which permitted him to weigh his patients, bed, bedclothes and all: he then measured the weight of his patients as nearly as possible before and after their deaths. He noticed a reduction in their weights, averaging a few grammes per patient, and was therefore able to conclude that this was the weight of the average soul – which, of course, left their bodies upon their deaths. An ingenious approach, but it has to be said that this sort of argument has not been found to carry very much conviction. It has never been demonstrated that there is any physically measurable force or entity which, when added to a lifeless body, produces a living one; and neither is it at all likely that any such thing will ever be found. It has generally been assumed that one of the features of the soul is its total non-physicality, and so we should not expect to be able to set up any kind of physical experiment which will enable us to demonstrate its presence (or, indeed, its absence). This means that it cannot be analysed, or even spoken of, in the same way as the physical body. (A further argument against the existence of a 'soul' thus understood arises here, in that it is difficult to see how such a completely non-physical thing could produce any kind of physical effect in the body which, allegedly, houses it.) Such attempts as these to put classical dualism on to a scientific footing are interesting, but I suspect that they will always be doomed to failure.

The second response we can make to the perceived opposition of reductionistic materialism and dualism is to note that there may actually be an alternative to these two extreme views. In order to see this, let us turn our thoughts to an examination of the mind–brain problem, on which much recent scientific and philosophical debate about the nature of human beings has focused.

The mind–brain problem

Inside each of our skulls there is a complicated, convoluted organ called a brain. How it works is still largely unclear; however, it's clear at least that it is composed of organic matter, and that as a general principle it works by the transport of small molecules within it, and by the passage of electrical signals between the cells it contains. What, if anything, is the difference between that physical organ and our minds – that sense we all possess of individuality, of consciousness, of being *me*? This appears to be a common enough human perception. But are we humans any more than the sum of all those electrical and chemical signals?

On the one hand, reductionistic materialist thinkers would reply 'No': on the other, dualist thinkers would say 'Yes' – there is something else, apart from these processes, which is responsible for who we are. Philosophers and scientists alike are divided on this issue. Some assert the sort of materialist argument considered above: others say that something else is going on. The philosopher Richard Swinburne, for example, professes an explicitly dualistic position. He asserts that brain-events are not the same as mental events, because 'Whatever ways an outsider has of finding out about my sensations I could use too (I could examine the evidence of stimulus and response), and yet I have a further way – by my experience of sensation.'[3] Swinburne has also commented:

> Those persons which are human beings (or men) living on Earth, have two parts linked together, body and soul. A man's body is that to which his physical properties belong. If a man weighs ten stone then his body weighs ten stone. A man's soul is that to which the (pure) mental properties of a man belong. If a man imagines a cat, then, the dualist will say, his soul imagines a cat.[4]

This is a very neat modern summary of the classic dualist position which has underpinned most Christian speculation regarding the nature of human beings.

It is not only philosophers who have defended dualism in recent years. A scientist who has put forward explicitly dualist views is John Eccles, a Nobel prize-winning neuroanatomist, who has studied the evolution of the human brain in great detail. He has concluded from his studies that they left him unable to account for the phenomenon of consciousness, and he therefore believes consciousness to have been implanted in human beings by God.[5] It should be added that this is not a particularly commonly held position among scientists in general. Nevertheless, we may note that dualist models of human beings are still being strongly championed.

Turning to more materialist interpretations of the mind–brain problem, the most straightforward would, of course, be that already discussed: to affirm that the words are more or less synonymous, and refer to the physical organ located in our skulls. It has been suggested that if mental events are caused by, or directly attributable to, physical events within the brain, then there cannot meaningfully be said to be any difference between the two. This would be the understanding of the reductionistic materialist view discussed above. Thus the philosopher John Searle writes that 'the mind and the body interact, but they are not two different things, since mental phenomena just are features of the brain'.[6] On Searle's understanding, mental phenomena are ultimately predictable and inevitable consequences of the properties and the physical ordering of matter in the brain. A contemporary scientist with a similar viewpoint is the physical chemist

P. W. Atkins, who has argued for the potential predictability of even so complex a phenomenon as the personality of an individual, simply from a detailed knowledge of that person's DNA.[7] A 'hard' materialist model has thus also had its champions in recent years.

So, are we faced with an either–or situation from the scientific and philosophical standpoint? Must we adopt either a dualistic position on the mind–brain problem, despite its associated difficulties, or else a reductionist–materialist position, which appears effectively to rule out the existence of minds as entities distinguishable from brains? I believe that a third alternative is possible here. The biologist J. Z. Young is essentially a materialist. He has written, 'Consciousness is an aspect of the functioning of the brain, not something that can exist apart from it,' and he asserts that 'All mental events are associated with events in the brain.' However, he goes on to write:

> It is tempting to say that events in the brain 'cause' mental events . . . The conception of a cause is notoriously difficult and ambiguous, but for the scientist it usually implies some sequence of material interaction with expenditure of energy. For this reason I find it undesirable to say that mental events are 'caused' by the brain.

Young adds the observation that the 'Complexity and adaptability of the brain means that precise forecasting of correlations between mental events and physical processes is never possible.'[8] This sort of materialistic approach is rather different to saying simply that human beings are no more than the sum of the physico–chemical processes which take place in our bodies. It suggests rather a model which presents our consciousness of ourselves as individuals as the result of an incredible complexity of events going on in our brains. This activity generates phenomena that are best thought of as emerging out of that complexity. It has also been suggested that our consciousness arises out of a process analogous to the running of incredibly complicated 'software' on the 'hardware' of those physical organs we call our brains.[9]

There are parallels between this model and the antireductionist views which were discussed in the last chapter. We have an interesting possibility beginning to emerge here. Instead of the strict alternatives of reductionistic materialism and dualism, the ideas that we are nothing but physical matter acting in complex but ultimately predictable ways, or else that we are compounded of two different elements, body and soul, it appears to be possible to say that we are material beings, but that there are aspects of ourselves that are emergent from the matter of which we are made, and irreducible to simple material considerations. We might characterize this approach as non-reductionistic materialism.

There is a considerable overlap between this sort of view and some recent theological speculation. Arthur Peacocke, a biochemist–theologian, espouses views very similar to J. Z. Young's. Peacocke has written: 'The mental activity which we call "consciousness" does not have to be predicated of some new entity, the "mind", but is an activity of matter which emerges when its units have evolved a particular kind of organized complexity.'[10] Russell Stannard, a physicist–theologian, writes in terms of a 'mapping' between different 'reality domains' – the physical and the mental:

> By a mapping, I mean that there can be a correspondence between a particular state in one reality domain and a particular state in another reality domain. The two are correlated such that if one occurs, the other occurs . . . This is not to say anything about why there should be this correspondence, or how the link between the two kinds of reality operates. I am not saying that the state in one reality domain 'causes' the state in the other to occur because of some action that takes place through the link between them.[11]

The idea of a correspondence that is non-causal appears again to be very close to Young's understanding of the relationship between mind and brain.

Let's now look more closely at the traditional Christian understanding of human beings, and at how this sort of approach might fit in with it.

The religious view

The Christian understanding of human nature, which is ultimately derived from inferences which can be made on the subject from the writings in the Bible, is that human beings are created by God, and are a part of his much bigger creation, the cosmos. Christians also believe that God loves his creation, and loves all human beings as a part of it. Human beings, whether they realize it or not, therefore stand in a position of *relationship* towards God; and it is an essential part of the Christian understanding of humanity to see it as standing within that relationship.

Our apprehension of God, and any approach which we may make towards him, occur not through purely physical means, though physical sensations may play a part in them. An early Christian writer, St Augustine, addressing God, wrote: 'You have made us for yourself, and our heart is restless until it rests in you.'[12] St Augustine identified within himself a sense of yearning, a sense many other people both before and since have felt, and it was this yearning which led him to God, in whom he found the total fulfilment of his yearnings. (He certainly tried very hard to find fulfilment in other ways before he turned to God: in his *Confessions* he has left us a fascinating account of his attempts to do so, prior to his turning to the Christian way.) Blaise Pascal, a seventeenth-century French mathematician and theological writer, makes the point that intellectual activity alone cannot satisfy this longing for God: 'It is the heart that perceives God and not the reason,' he wrote. He shared St Augustine's conviction that happiness and fulfilment are only to be found in God: 'If man was not made for God, why is he only happy in God?'[13] Friedrich Schleiermacher, a German theologian of the early nineteenth century, wrote about a 'Feeling of absolute dependency', which he believed was common to all people. Schleiermacher believed that this feeling draws people towards God, as the one on whom all life is dependent. Our feeling of absolute dependency, Schleiermacher suggested, is what brings about a 'God-consciousness' within us.[14] In all these writers, and indeed in many others, we see reflected the idea propounded by Christianity, that human beings are intended to exist in a relationship with God, but that that relationship has in some sense been soured: this idea is of course given a dramatic, poetic form in the story of the 'fall' of Adam and Eve in the book of Genesis (see Genesis, chapter 3). Reconciliation between God and humankind is therefore necessary. This is the meaning behind the Christian doctrine of the Atonement: it is an 'at-one-ment', a making as one, of the two parties involved in the rift between God and humankind. This is viewed by Christians as being the greatest of the achievements brought about by the life and death of Jesus Christ.[15]

Such yearnings and feelings as those which St Augustine, Pascal and Schleiermacher identified cannot be given any physical, or physiological, location. There is not (or at any rate, there has not yet been discovered) a part of the brain, or of the body, which is fulfilled or satisfied by the activity of such feelings as those of which these theologians speak. (It would indeed be fascinating if such an area were ever to be discovered.) Rather, Christians have tended to think in dualistic terms, believing such feelings and yearnings to originate in the soul of the individual. This idea is certainly there in the Bible: indeed, some of Jesus' own words reported there would appear to support such a position.[16] However, the dualistic ideas expressed in the mainstream Christianity of the early Church perhaps owe as much to the ideas of the Greek philosopher Plato and his followers as they do to the Bible.[17] In the early Church, the soul came to be seen as that which is immortal, which is capable of thought, of reasoning, of aesthetic judgement, even of eventual union with God; whilst the body, on the other hand, was viewed as mortal, as concerned only with physical satisfaction, and even (in the thinking of some early Christian sects that were later regarded as heretical, such as the Manichees) as inherently evil.

Another way of thinking about the same thing is to see human beings as physical bodies that are made to live by the presence within them of some 'divine spark' which animates them. Such a view might follow from the Old Testament account of the creation, in which God is represented as breathing life into the inanimate body of Adam, the first man (see Genesis 2.7). This is the position sometimes known as *vitalism*. Again, though, something extra besides our physical bodies has to be assumed to exist in order to make up a full, complete human being; and that something could presumably never be discovered or analysed from a scientific point of view.

However we regard the situation, there's no getting away from it: the traditional Christian understanding of human beings is unmistakably dualistic. It therefore stands in sharp contrast to the materialist understandings advocated by many scientists. Anyone wishing to argue towards harmony between the traditional religious and scientific understandings is faced with a dilemma at this point, to which, I believe, there are two possible responses.

The first response is simply to accept that these positions are irreconcilable, to re-state them, and to invite people to choose between them on the basis of which is most fully compatible with their own personal experiences as human beings. Many people, on this basis, would probably say that they are conscious of having a component of their being that is not satisfactorily explained by the materialist view, and would therefore adopt a more or less dualist one – taking on board as much or as little traditional Christian teaching about the soul as they felt appropriate. I, too, frequently feel the intuitive appeal in this sort of understanding of human beings as physical bodies animated by non-physical souls. However, I am far from being wholly convinced by the classical dualist position myself, and I am also aware that there are many people who find materialist arguments compelling; and for both of these reasons I think that the second way out of the dilemma which I have posed is preferable to this one. That way is to re-think the classical Christian dualistic position in the light of contemporary scientific understandings of how humans work. I believe such a response as this to be both necessary and helpful.

By way of justifying such a re-thinking, we should note that it is debatable to what extent dualism is a vital element of Christianity, and to what extent it is simply a bit of metaphysical baggage which Christianity picked up in its formative years, as the best available explanation for natural phenomena at the time when the biblical texts were being analysed and interpreted within the early Church. (If the latter were the case, then dualistic ideas would of course have persisted ever since, in the minds of those influenced by such analyses and interpretations.) It has in fact been suggested that the world-view of many biblical writers, particularly those of the Old Testament, is not straightforwardly dualistic in this manner, but rather that the governing paradigm through much of the Bible is the view that human beings are psychosomatic – that is, soul–body – unities. Some modern theologians have also argued in favour of this understanding of human beings. Arthur Peacocke, for example, maintains that such a view 'Is in fact quite acceptable to Christian theology – and is indeed also consistent with Biblical views concerning human nature,' provided that the events taking place in the mind/brain which we describe as 'mental' events are recognized as having a reality which is not reducible to purely material language.[18]

Let us now return to those non-reductionistic materialist ideas which we were considering earlier. We saw that they suggested a way in which an essentially materialistic understanding of human beings, seeing us as psychosomatic unities, can yet enable us to speak meaningfully of phenomena that may not be reduced to physico–chemical processes in a straightforward way. I believe that they can provide us with a model of how human beings work which harmonizes well with the Christian view, but which does not have to assume dualistic ideas for no good reason. We have seen that there are some properties of things that cannot be attributed simply to the actions of their parts, but arise out of those parts acting together as a whole. I think it not too fanciful to speak of mind and brain, or even body and soul, as separate functions of matter – maybe even as separate entities – even though there is no extra thing there physically to differentiate between them, in the way that vitalists have asserted.

There is a fundamental complexity to human beings that reductionistic materialist understandings will never fully be capable of penetrating. Quite simply, we frequently do not function as the complex machines which, such materialist understandings of human beings would urge us to think, is all that we are. Human consciousness is a more complex phenomenon than this analysis would have us believe.[19] (In any case, as we have seen, even if we *were* simply machines, our understanding of those machines will always be limited by our capacity to measure the physical events which characterize them.) Not only at the quantum level, but also at the level of complex organisms, the determinist understanding of the way the physical world operates has to be regarded as inadequate, despite its many successes in the intervening levels.

But I don't think it is necessary to go all the way over to the dualists' position. If we think about human beings as having aspects of our humanity which arise out of our existence as the complex organic creatures that we are, we do not need to postulate the existence of any non-material 'soul', which exists separately from the body but somehow in conjunction with it. Rather, we may think in terms of human beings having aspects of ourselves which are not reducible to simple machine-like physico–chemical functions of our bodies, but which nevertheless arise out of that physico–chemical functioning. Such aspects of our humanity might include character, emotion, aesthetic response, even the sort of theological yearnings described by St Augustine, by Pascal and by Schleiermacher: in other words, all those attributes that were once considered to be properties of the soul.

This sort of view does not deny the validity of modern scientific thinking about human beings, whilst it does avoid the outright dualism that has been the traditional Christian response to it. It affirms human beings as being more than 'just' physical bodies, without needing to introduce any other entities in order to say what else we are. A human being in his or her totality may have needs that no part of him or her is capable of experiencing in isolation; and perhaps the need for God, when it is experienced, operates at that level.

If we think of our minds, and our souls – all those non-material things which (it is usually felt) make us the persons that we are – as being emergent qualities, arising in a non-reducible way from the physical matter which comprises our bodies, this also makes sense of the fact that we are conscious of persisting as individual beings even though the physical stuff of which we are made is constantly changing. There is a continuity between 'me' as I am today and the 'me' I remember being as a child, even though there is probably only a small percentage of atoms and molecules still present in my body that were there when I was, say, five years old. 'I' am a constant, even though the stuff of which I am made is constantly changing.

A rather more complex problem arises, though, if we ask, 'What happens when we die?' If our souls are related to our bodies in the way I have described, it might be thought that the traditional Christian understanding of our souls as immortal has to be jettisoned. With the death and decomposition of our bodies, the qualities that emerged from them presumably also die. Yet since it is our souls, those parts of us that most truly represent who we really are, that relate to God, is it not possible to think in terms of the survival of our souls after death, as ideas or memories in the mind of God? The Christian doctrine of the resurrection then holds out the hope that this survival may be made real for each individual, through God bringing about our continued existence, possibly recreated in some new form. John Polkinghorne has expressed this idea as follows:

> The real me is the immensely complicated 'pattern' in which these ever-changing atoms are organized. It seems to me to be an intelligible and coherent hope that God will remember the pattern that is me and recreate it in a new environment of his choosing, by his great act of final resurrection. Christian belief in a destiny beyond death has always centred on resurrection, not survival . . . It's the pattern that signifies, not the matter that makes it up.[20]

The cosmologist Frank Tipler has suggested that modern physics can also provide a basis for thinking in such terms as these, and indeed goes so far as to urge that 'Physics will permit the resurrection to eternal life of everyone who has lived, is living and will live.'[21]

Stephen Hawking, in his best-selling book *A Brief History of Time*, suggests that it may be the ultimate goal of the human intellect to 'Know the mind of God.'[22] Perhaps we might say rather that it is the ultimate destiny of human beings actually to become parts of the mind of God, and thence to attain to an entirely new form of physical existence. Quite what that existence will be like is beyond our powers to envisage, but it will presumably be very different to the kind of life which we experience now. It is interesting to note that this understanding of the resurrection life as radically different to the present one is in accord with the views of St Paul, expressed in the Bible: 'What is sown is perishable, what is raised is imperishable . . . It is sown a physical body, it is raised a spiritual body' (1 Corinthians 15. 42–44).

Antireductionism in the biological sciences

It is very interesting to note that actually within the biological and medical sciences the introduction of antireductionist ideas at a theoretical level has recently been taking place. For over a century, the evolutionary theories that originated with Darwin have been a commonplace in these sciences. With the arrival of molecular biology, the importance within the evolutionary process has been thrown on to the genes which all living organisms contain, and which govern the reproduction of those organisms. (Genes are basically very large organic molecules, based on nucleic acids.) The evolution of more and more sophisticated forms of life is understood to occur by natural selection, operating on the variety of organisms produced through the mutation – the gradual, chance transformation – of the genes which they contain. Richard Dawkins, a biologist who espouses this sort of approach, therefore represents the gene as the basic unit governing evolution. His doctrine of the 'selfish gene' is designed to make the point that larger organisms are to be understood as the product of gene-based evolution, and that, since this evolution is totally random and 'blind', no significances to life based on any other assumption than that of its random origin is to be considered tenable. According to Dawkins, genes determine the attributes of bodies, which are developed in order to produce more genes as effectively as possible. He writes of genes, 'They are the replicators and we are their survival machines.'[23]

However, in opposition to this, some physiologists have recently re-asserted the importance of the *organism* in science. D. Noble and C. A. R. Boyd have suggested that genes are in fact best pictured as 'Severely restricted prisoners rather than as free-roving "selfish" entities: prisoners of the successful physiological systems carrying them.'[24] The complex structures of organisms impose restrictions on the genes they contain, affecting and containing their activity. This may be seen as a noteworthy example of the operation of 'top-down causation' in the scientific field, providing another example of the scientific relevance of antireductionist thinking.

I would therefore urge that modern understandings suggest that the old scientific/materialist and theological/dualist understandings of humankind are not as utterly incompatible as we might have thought. A distinctively Christian, non-reductionistic materialism points the way towards the reconciliation of these apparently opposed understandings of the nature of humanity. So far, though, our discussion of scientific views about human beings has been confined to the physical and biological sciences, and these are of course not the only scientific disciplines that have given rise to theories about how human beings function. The psychological and social sciences too have contributed much material, however hotly debated some of it may be, to our understanding of what it is that makes us tick. I should therefore like to conclude this chapter by looking at the theories of two of the great pioneers of psychology, the psychoanalysts Sigmund Freud and Carl Gustav Jung, in order to supplement all that has been discussed so far. Interestingly, the views these two men had about religion could not have been more different, as we shall see.

The psychological sciences

Freud

Many of the ideas of Sigmund Freud have become very well known, and it is surely not exaggerating unduly to describe him as one of the most influential and innovative thinkers of the twentieth century. There can be hardly an aspect of late twentieth-century Western life and culture that has not felt in some measure the consequences of his ideas. Freud's background was very much in the materialist physiological school of Helmholz, mentioned above. Throughout his career he thought of himself first and foremost as a scientist, and he developed his theories convinced of their scientificity. These theories were, after all, based on the empirical observations which he made of himself and of his patients. The data used by Freud were derived largely from the dreams and other unconscious foibles of his patients, such as involuntary errors ('Freudian slips'), and from the physical symptoms which the patients manifested. Freud developed the technique of 'free association' in order to analyse the psychologically significant content which these dreams, errors or symptoms possessed. This technique involved simply inviting his patients to say the first things that came into their heads about these phenomena. Based on the observations which he made, Freud slowly developed his theories of human mental behaviour. He proposed that the human psyche is comprised of three parts, which he named the ego, the superego and the id. The ego is the self's organized, realistic component: the superego is the sense of conscience, which criticizes and can restrict the activities of the ego; and the id is the uncoordinated, instinctual part of the self. Our overall functioning as human beings is governed by these separate components of the psyche, acting together or in opposition to one another.

As is well known, Freud believed sexuality to underlie much of human behaviour, and sexual trauma in some form to give rise to the behaviour of psychologically disturbed people. He noted that the unveiling of the origins of sexual traumas, often through the interpretation of the patient's dreams and through discussions with a psychotherapist, frequently led to the disappearance of the neurotic symptoms the patient had been displaying. As his studies progressed, he felt compelled to locate the likely source of the trauma further and further back in a person's life, finally developing a theory of infant sexuality.

Critics of Freud, of his theories and of the methods by which he arrived at them, have been manifold and vociferous. We have already noted that Popper's proposal of a criterion of demarcation between science and non-science was designed, at least in part, in order to show that Freud's theories could not claim the scientific status that Freud insisted they deserved. Those methods do seem to have been effective in many cases, however; and some of Freud's case studies make fascinating reading simply because, despite the apparently outlandish ideas that lie behind them, they did actually bring about the cures of his patients. Although Freud's theories may not be reduced to the functioning of physico–chemical processes in the human body, he still believed human mental behaviour to follow laws in the same way that such bodily physico–chemical behaviour does, and he saw his life's work in terms of his elucidation of those laws.

What about Freud's views on religion? They, too, are derived from his materialistic approach to the analysis of human behaviour. Religious beliefs, Freud argued, are forms of illusion generated by the desire to see wishes fulfilled: 'Religious ideas . . . are illusions, fulfilments of the oldest, strongest and most urgent wishes of mankind.'[25] Like all such illusions, they are unhealthy and should be overcome by rational human beings. Having established that unconscious desires leading to suppressed wishes can produce hysterical symptoms in a neurotic patient, Freud went on to assert his belief that religious belief was essentially a form of collective hysteria. 'One might venture,' he writes, 'to regard obsessional neurosis as a pathological counterpart of the formation of a religion, and to describe that neurosis as an individual religiosity and religion as a universal obsessional neurosis.'[26]

Freud's religious writings are largely based on the studies made by anthropologists of the religious practices of 'primitive' peoples, such as Australian aborigines. When he turns to the Judaeo–Christian religious tradition, which he assumes to originate from the same sorts of practices, his views make for very entertaining reading indeed. He asserts, for example, that 'The beginnings of religion, morals, society and art converge in the Oedipus complex',[27] and that 'Yahweh [the god of the Jews] was unquestionably a volcano God.'[28] Freud also argued that religion is an entirely man-made phenomenon. He maintained that religions were originally designed to help people to overcome feelings of guilt derived from a primal act of parricide, in which a group of brothers killed their father and then suffered great pangs of remorse. There is no such entity as God: ideas about him derive from primitive projections of emotions connected with fatherhood. One shudders to think what Freud's relationship with his own father must have been like to have produced such a view as this (it has, incidentally, been characterized as 'Ambivalence . . . in which hate mingled with fear and pity, as well as with love.'[29]) The persistence of religions in developed societies Freud attributes to the effectiveness of religions in general as a means of social control.

Freud's ideas about the illusory nature of religious beliefs follow logically enough from his underlying assumptions about human beings and about the origins of all forms of human behaviour in physico–chemical processes within our bodies. At first sight, his ideas about religions as providing a form of wish-fulfilment appear quite persuasive. Death, for example, is universally regarded as something frightening; so the idea that religions evolved to cater for the urgent desire of people to see meaning and purpose in life, by telling them about a life after death, would appear to carry conviction. On this understanding, religions are seen as belief systems which are geared towards the future, promising rewards in some imagined future life in return for adherence to a required form of social behaviour in the present. (I dare say that there are indeed some people today who, in their practice of their religion, do actually think in terms of the future happiness that their virtuous actions in the present are 'buying' for them. In the case of Christianity, it is surely ironic in the extreme that this basically selfish attitude should underlie the practice of a religion that proclaims selflessness to be the greatest of virtues.)

Attractive as this understanding of the origins of religions may be, it is fundamentally incorrect. John Bowker has pointed out that the earliest forms of religion either do not posit any kind of afterlife at all, or at most suggest that the afterworld is a rather shadowy and unexciting place to be. In Psalm 39, for example, the writer addresses God thus:

> You have made my days but a handsbreadth,
>   and my whole span is as nothing before you.
> Surely every man though he stand secure is but breath,
> And lives as a passing shadow . . .
> I am but a stranger with you,
> A passing guest as all my fathers were.
> Turn your eyes from me that I may smile again,
> Before I go hence and am no more.
>
> (Psalm 39. 5–6, 14–15)

There is little here to suggest boundless optimism regarding a life beyond this one! Bowker writes:

> At the root of all major, continuing religions, earliest speculation about death did not produce a belief that there is a desirable life with God beyond this life, after death . . . This means that the widespread account of the origin of religion, that it lies in the human fear of death and the construction of compensatory but illusory paradises, is certainly wrong, so far as we can judge from the evidence that survives.[30]

Later religious thinking within different traditions may postulate an afterlife of some sort, but it does not appear to play any part in the origins of religion, as Freud urges.

Freud, then, saw religious beliefs as being nothing but potentially dangerous sources of illusion – dangerous in terms of the symptoms which they can engender in an individual believer. He did, however, acknowledge that religious faith could be useful for those who profess it, since 'Devout believers are safeguarded in a high degree against the risk of certain neurotic illnesses' – even though this is believed by Freud to be because 'Their acceptance of the universal neurosis spares them the task of constructing a personal one'![31] For Jung, however, religions were not psychic diseases, but rather completely the opposite: they were a means of effecting psychic cures.

Jung

Jung began his psychoanalytical career as an ardent pupil of Freud's, and his subsequent split with his erstwhile master may be followed in their fascinating correspondence.[32] Following that split, Jung's theories developed rather differently to Freud's. To summarize those theories very briefly, Jung, like Freud, believed that the human personality is composite: that there are within each of us a variety of forces, pulling us in different directions. These forces Jung perceived to present themselves in certain archetypal forms in the dreams of his patients. (Again like Freud, Jung attached a great deal of importance to the analysis of dreams.) Among the components that each of us possesses as a part of his or her psyche Jung identified a component which possesses the opposite sex. This he called the 'anima' in the case of a man, and the 'animus' in the case of a woman. Each of us contains a 'shadow' personality, compounded of those attributes which for whatever reason we regard as evil, or corrupt, or wrong. Each of us, moreover, has access to a 'collective unconscious', in which is stored part of the cumulative wisdom of humankind. The goal of human psychic life is to achieve the harmonious integration of these and other components to produce what Jung called the 'Self', this journey towards Selfhood being termed the 'individuation process'.

For Freud, God was an illusion, or at best an infantile projection of feelings about the father. Jung, on the other hand, was not afraid to write about God as a reality experienced both by himself and by his patients. He believed that the healing of patients involved bringing about their wholeness as human beings, and a part of this process involved facing and embracing whatever ideas of God they might possess. For Jung, God is an archetype to be integrated into the Self, along with other archetypes. And not only is God to be regarded as real: Jung further believed the person of Jesus Christ to be of great significance in facilitating the individuation process, since 'Christ is our nearest analogy of the Self and its meaning.'[33] Jung affirmed religions in general as being of great therapeutic value, believing them to be 'Systems of healing for psychic illness'.[34]

It is fascinating to speculate on the possible coming together of the two disciplines of science and theology in Jung's work (like Freud, Jung insisted that his work was scientific). Such speculation has certainly fuelled the pens of many Jungian devotees, some of whom have urged that orthodox theologians ought to take on board many of his ideas. But was Jung truly a scientist, as a present-day natural scientist might understand the meaning of that word? And was he a theologian, as some of his supporters claim: do his ideas make sense to modern-day theologians?[35]

For Jung, his work was scientific because it was empirical: it was based on his observations. The empirical material used by Jung was derived from three different sources: hypnosis, association tests, and dream analysis. He soon found the results of hypnosis experiments less than satisfactory, as Freud had also found, and so his early researches were carried out largely by means of association tests, in which the subject is invited to respond to a stimulus word with the first response that comes into his or her head. However, in his later writings, in which his ideas about God are developed furthest, the empirical material upon which Jung's ideas are grounded appears to be principally the dreams of himself and his patients. Although the data which these produce are rather more vague and imprecise than the data produced by association tests, Jung continued to maintain that the theories which he based on them had an empirical basis.

Our response to Jung's claim that his work is scientific will depend on what we mean by science. If we apply Popper's understanding of science to Jung, we would have to say that, since it is difficult to imagine any kind of observation which could refute a theory of Jung's (those theories tending to be so imprecisely formulated), then those theories are not scientific. However, Popper's definition of what constitutes a science is very much in terms of an 'intellect alone' discipline; and since Jung repeatedly insisted that there are factors other than purely intellectual ones to be considered in constructing psychological theories, Jung himself would doubtless have excluded psychology from the realm of science, as defined by Popper. On the other hand, Kuhn's or Feyerabend's critiques of science might be able to accommodate Jung and his theories, since they allow for the operation of other than purely rational processes in the practice of science. Feyerabend would in any case doubtless approve of Jung's theories as helpful to people, whether or not they are in any formal sense 'scientific': their validity derives from their effect. Jung's own axiom, 'The real is what works,'[36] in a sense harmonizes well with Feyerabend's maxim, 'Anything goes'.

Let us now consider whether or not Jung may be regarded as an orthodox theologian. Here, of course, the answer to our question will depend on what we mean by 'orthodox'. Jung makes it quite clear that he is in no doubt at all about the existence of God: 'God is an obvious psychic and non-physical fact, i.e., a fact that can be established psychically but not physically,' he writes.[37] Jung also makes frequent references to the person and character of Christ, so that it seems reasonable to describe his theology as a Christian theology. However, theologians and Christian writers are divided over Jung's approach. Some find it both helpful and thoroughly consistent with orthodox Christian theology: for example, Christopher Bryant has urged that Jung's ideas can bring practical illumination to the Christian life, and Victor White has urged that Jung's theories are compatible with the classic Roman Catholic theology of St Thomas Aquinas.[38] However, other writers have not been quite so certain about Jung's orthodoxy. Perhaps their uncertainties derive from Jung's use of the word 'God'.

Jung has written that his understanding of this word is not the same as that of a theologian who would wish to refer to transcendent reality outside our experiences. More specifically, he has stated: 'Psychologically . . . God is the name for a complex of ideas grouped around a powerful feeling.'[39] It would appear, then, that in contrast to the metaphysical, 'other' God of most theologians, Jung would wish to deal solely with the subjective, empirically observable, internal complexes of his patients – and it is to certain of these that he gives the name 'God' in his writings. Jung does not deny the existence of a more orthodox, metaphysical God: he simply states that we may not gain access to this God by psychological means. For Jung, 'Religion means dependence on and submission to the irrational facts of experience.'[40] Speculation beyond such facts is not an area in which he desires to dabble.

Jung's 'theology' is clearly somewhat different to that of most Christian theologians. It might be argued that the words 'God', 'Christ' and 'Soul' (to mention just three) need never have been introduced into his writings by Jung at all, and that his ideas might have been better expressed in more obviously neo-Freudian terms – 'complexes', 'projections' and so on. Whilst this is in many ways true, it is important to remember that Jung's ideas constitute not just a theory but also a practical approach to living. If the language which Jung used with his patients was, when appropriate, theological or religious in tone, and if this effected their cure, then, as an accurate reporter of his work, this is the language which it is necessary for

Jung to use in his writings – no matter what interpretations he might give to it in order to make it more accessible to psychologists. A wide variety of metaphysical ideas underlies the thinking of different theologians: it might be urged that there is no reason why Jung's ideas, despite their unusual basis in empirical psychology, should not stand alongside them. As a practically formulated, useful construct, his understanding of God can only aid and further the interaction of theology with the broader field of human enquiry, scientific or otherwise. That his model may require modification is something that Jung himself would have taken for granted. The following remark is typical: 'My work has many weak spots and gaps, for which I crave the reader's indulgence . . . Somebody, after all, had to set the ball rolling.'[41]

We therefore see that whilst Freud remained an atheist, who had no room for religions in his theories other than as causes of neuroses, Jung, in sharp contrast, gives us an understanding of what human beings are, which is deeply religious, albeit without many of the traditional religious trappings. Both Freud and Jung also insisted on the scientific basis of their ideas: perhaps this in part accounts for the popularity which they have enjoyed. I suspect that whether an individual finds Freud's, or Jung's, or some other model of the individual the most compelling will be largely a matter of individual preference. Personally, I find it very tempting to think that in Jung's ideas we may see a potential coming together of scientific and theological concepts of what it is to be a conscious individual: we may catch in them an exciting glimpse of an all-embracing account of what we mean by 'I'. Having said this, it must be added that Jung's exclusively interior God does not fully square with the God of Christian tradition. The Christian God, it has always been insisted, is both interior and exterior, immanent and transcendent: that is to say, God is both experienced inwardly (in whatever way) by the individual believer; and yet also has an independent existence, an independent being, 'other' to the believer. God is present with us, it is asserted, as well as being beyond us, both physically and conceptually. Some of these traditional understandings, and paradoxes, about God will be considered in the course of the next chapter.

NOTES

1. Quoted in Ernest Jones' fascinating biography *The Life and Work of Sigmund Freud*: in the abridged version (Pelican, 1964), pp. 62–3.
2. John Bowker offers a judicious and cautious assessment of the significance of NDEs. He writes: 'Near-death experience makes clear . . . that dying can be one of the good human experiences (this is very extensively reported), and that in relation to the body and its death,

the self is clearly (i.e., experiences itself as) independent of its body; or, if that seems too strong a statement, that at least the experience of being thus independent is so unequivocal and real that no other language is able to describe it.' (J. Bowker, *The Meanings of Death* (Cambridge University Press, 1991), p. 224.) For a more detailed assessment, see, for example, Carol Zaleski's *Otherworld Journeys* (Oxford University Press, 1987).

3. Richard Swinburne, *The Evolution of the Soul* (Oxford University Press, 1986), p. 60. Swinburne has written several fascinating books approaching belief in God from the point of view of the modern philosopher (see, for example, his *The Existence of God* (Oxford University Press: revised edition, 1991).

4. R. Swinburne, *The Evolution of the Soul*, p. 145.

5. John Eccles' fascinating researches leading to this remarkable conclusion are set out in his book *The Evolution of the Brain* (Routledge, 1989).

6. John Searle, *Minds, Brains and Science* (BBC Publications, 1984), p. 26.

7. P. W. Atkins, *The Creation* (W. H. Freeman and Company, 1981), p. 2.

8. The quotations are all from J. Z. Young, *Philosophy and the Brain* (Oxford University Press, 1987), pp. 12–15.

9. Daniel Dennett has expounded precisely this thesis in his book *Consciousness Explained* (Penguin, 1992). This is a fascinating book; regrettably, however, the present writer found that it didn't quite live up to the high expectations raised by its title.

10. A. Peacocke, *Intimations of Reality* (University of Notre Dame Press, 1984), p. 74.

11. R. Stannard, *Grounds for Reasonable Belief* (Scottish Academic Press, 1989), pp. 129–30.

12. St Augustine, *Confessions*, trans. Henry Chadwick (Oxford University Press, 1992), p. 3. The *Confessions* throws much light on this fascinating, complex and extremely influential Saint, and also serves as an accessible introduction to much of his philosophical and theological thought.

13. B. Pascal, *Pensées*, trans. A. J. Krailsheimer (Penguin, 1966), pp. 154 and 146. Pascal is a fascinating figure: a mathematician who laid the basis of modern probability theory, a physicist who performed experiments with barometers, and a man who, after a profound religious experience, became a passionate Christian apologist. The *Pensées* are a collection of notes that were to form the basis of a reasoned defence of the Christian faith: sadly, Pascal did not live to complete it.

14. B. A. Gerrish's *A Prince of the Church: Schleiermacher and the Beginnings of Modern Theology* (SCM Press, 1984) is a readable introduction to Schleiermacher's thought.

15. For a discussion of a variety of ways in which this Atonement may be understood, see F. W. Dillistone, *The Christian Understanding of the Atonement* (SCM Press, 1984). See also A. Peacocke, *Theology for a Scientific Age* (enlarged edition, SCM Press, 1993) especially chapter 15.

16. For example, the saying 'Do not fear those who kill the body but cannot kill the soul' (Matthew 10. 28).

17. Plato's theory of the soul's immortality (in contrast to the body's mortality) is set out in the dialogue *Phaedo*, in which Socrates states, 'When death comes to a man, his mortal part, it seems, dies, but the immortal part goes away unharmed and undestroyed, withdrawing from death . . . It is perfectly certain that the soul is immortal and imperishable, and our souls will exist somewhere in another world' (*Phaedo* 106 E–107 A, trans. H. N. Fowler (Loeb Classical Library, 1914)). The soul is further characterized as being 'Like the divine and immortal and intellectual and uniform and indissoluble and ever unchanging' (ibid., 80 B). *Phaedo* also tells most movingly of Socrates' own death, and gives a remarkable picture of heaven as the ultimate destination of all good-living souls. In the dialogue *Timaeus* Plato writes of the soul's relationship to the body thus: 'God has given to each of us, as his genius, that kind of soul which is housed in the top of our body and which raises us up – seeing that we are not an earthly but a heavenly plant – up from earth towards our kindred in heaven' (*Timaeus*, 90 A, trans. R. G. Bury (Loeb Classical Library, 1929)). In addition, the celebrated myth of Er in *The Republic* speaks of the adventures of a soul which leaves a body on its death, and presents the doctrine of the transmigration of souls, suggesting that the souls of the dead are subsequently re-born in new bodies (*The Republic*, 614 A ff.). This last doctrine, of course, was not taken up by Christian writers on this subject, since it is incompatible with Christian ideas about human individuality.

Plato's ideas were greatly developed by various philosophers, notably in later antiquity by Plotinus (3rd century CE), from whom was derived much subsequent Christian speculation in this area. Plotinus speaks of the soul as 'fallen', although it retains something of its contact with the higher 'Realm of the Intellect' from which it has descended, and to which it may return through contemplation. In the meantime, it is 'Bitter and miserable in durance in body, a victim to troubles and desires and fears and all forms of evil, the body its prison or its tomb, the cosmos its cave or cavern' (*Fourth Ennead*, Eighth Tractate, ch. 3: trans. S. MacKenna (Penguin, 1991), p. 337).

The dependence of later Christian theology on such writings as these cannot be over-emphasized. Indeed, Dean Inge went so far as to write that there is an 'Utter impossibility of excising Platonism from Christianity without tearing Christianity to pieces' (quoted in Bertrand Russell, *History of Western Philosophy* (Unwin, 1979), p. 289).

18. A. Peacocke, *Theology for a Scientific Age*, p. 160.
19. This psychological complexity is explored by Dostoevsky in his *Notes from Underground*. This novella is a kind of thought experiment, an exercise in imagining how a person might respond to an inexorably mechanistic world-view. In it, Dostoevsky writes:

> If men really turned out to be piano-keys [i.e. behaved in a deterministic fashion], and if it was proved to them by science and mathematics, even then they would not see reason, but on the contrary would deliberately do something out of sheer ingratitude in order, in fact, to have their own way ... If you say that all this ... could also be reduced to tables, so that the mere possibility of taking it into account beforehand would put a stop to it, and reason would still hold sway – in that case men would deliberately go mad, so as not to possess reason, and thus still get their own way! I believe this, I am prepared to answer for it, because it seems to me that the whole business of humanity consists solely in this – that a man should constantly prove to himself that he is a man and not a sprig in a barrel-organ! (*Notes from Underground*, trans. Jessie Coulson (Penguin, 1972), p. 38.)

20. J. Polkinghorne, *Quarks, Chaos and Christianity* (Triangle, 1994), pp. 92–3.
21. F. J. Tipler, *The Physics of Immortality* (Macmillan, 1995), p. 1.
22. S. Hawking, *A Brief History of Time* (Bantam Press, 1988), p. 193.
23. R. Dawkins, *The Selfish Gene* (2nd edition, Oxford University Press, 1989), p. 35.
24. C. A. R. Boyd and D. Noble, 'The Challenge of Integrative Physiology', in *The Logic of Life*, eds C. A. R. Boyd and D. Noble (Oxford University Press, 1993), p. 5. The general tone of this collection of essays is set in its foreword, in which Professor Sir James Black writes: 'Hopes of realizing the optimistic forecasts about the benefits that molecular biology will bring to pharmacology are likely, I believe, to be circumscribed by the state of physiological knowledge, models and concepts' (p. vii). In other words, no matter how far our understanding of the biochemistry underlying the behaviour of creatures such as ourselves may advance, we are likely to remain dependent in practical matters on our understanding, not of our genes, but of the larger organs of which we are made.
25. Freud's writings on religion are collected in volumes 12 and 13 of the Penguin Freud Library (1991). The quotation here is from *The Future of an Illusion* in vol. 12, p. 212.
26. Freud, *Obsessions and Religion*, Penguin Freud Library, vol. 13, p. 40: cf. *The Future of an Illusion*, Penguin Freud Library, vol. 12, p. 226.
27. Freud, *Totem and Taboo*, Penguin Freud Library, vol. 13, p. 219.
28. Freud, *Moses and Monotheism*, Penguin Freud Library, vol. 13, p. 273.
29. R. Wollheim, *Freud* (Fontana, 1973), p. 19.
30. J. Bowker, *The Meanings of Death* (Cambridge University Press, 1991), p. 29.
31. Freud, *The Future of an Illusion*, Penguin Freud Library, vol. 12, p. 227.
32. See, for example, the slightly abridged edition published by Penguin (*The Freud/Jung Letters*, 1991).
33. C. G. Jung, *Collected Works*, vol. 9, pt ii, (2nd edition, 1968), para. 79. The *Collected Works* (*CW*) of Jung are published in 20-odd volumes by Routledge and Kegan Paul, translated by R. F. C. Hull and others. Note that references to CW are to volume followed by *paragraph* number.

Volume 7 of this series, *Two Essays in Analytical Psychology*, is particularly recommended to any who wish to familiarize themselves with Jung's work.
34. Jung, *CW*, vol. 11, (2nd edition, 1969), para. 531.
35. The following is an abbreviated version of my article 'C. G. Jung: Scientist–Theologian?' which first appeared in *Theology*, xcv (1992), pp. 270 ff.

36. Jung, *CW*, vol. 7, (2nd edition, 1966), para. 353.
37. Jung, *CW*, vol. 11, (2nd edition, 1969), para. 751.
38. See C. Bryant, *Jung and the Christian Way* (Darton, Longman and Todd, 1983), and V. White, *God and the Unconscious* (Fontana, 1960).
39. Jung, *CW* vol. 5, (2nd edition, 1967), para. 128.
40. Jung, *CW*, vol. 10, (1964), para. 505.
41. Jung, *CW*, vol. 3, (1960), para. 316.

4

Sources and methods

There were more than nine hundred known gods on the disc, and research theologians were discovering more every year.

Terry Pratchett, *Mort*

We have seen that the methods employed by the two disciplines of science and theology have some things in common. Both are basically intellectual pursuits (although in each both rational and non-rational, subjective and objective factors have a part to play). Each of them therefore will handle and process the data at its disposal in a similar way, using the analytical techniques appropriate to it. However, in approaching the subject of the sources used by scientists and theologians in pursuing their investigations we appear really to be hitting on a fundamental difference between these two disciplines. For a scientist, the source of the data which he or she gathers and uses is the physical world, even though (as we have seen) the observation and interpretation of that data takes place in ways less 'objective' that we might perhaps have thought. The physical world is, of course, an enormously rich and varied source of information, constantly surprising, constantly yielding fresh insights. On the other hand, for the theologian – the Christian theologian, at any rate – the principal sources used are the Bible and the writings of earlier theologians: a clearly defined and more or less self-contained body of literature. To be sure, minor details may be clarified as evidence from new manuscripts comes to light, and new interpretations of old texts may be 'tested' against earlier writings; but it would seem that the sources used by the theologian are basically 'closed' rather than 'open', circumscribed rather than ever-widening with advances in our understanding. Given this fact, too, it might be assumed that the theologian will necessarily be more obliged than the scientist to use his or her imagination in expounding the available information, rather than sticking strictly to an objective analysis of the given data.

Let's now examine these ideas a little more closely, to see if science and theology are as different in these respects as we might think.

The sources used by science

Consider the wide variety of material used by the scientist. That material is derived from investigations at many different levels. The physicist 'looks at' sub-atomic and atomic particles, and the forces governing their interactions. To do this, he or she will use highly sophisticated (and probably highly expensive!) apparatus, and this apparatus will yield images requiring considerable manipulation and interpretation to make sense of them. This is of course where the current paradigm operating within physics comes in, as we have seen. Tracks in bubble chambers, spots on fluorescent screens, disturbances of some material which is expected to interact with the entity which the physicist is expecting to 'see': these may all be interpreted as indicating the presence of particles or waves that could not possibly be seen with optical magnification systems, let alone with the naked eye.

The chemist 'looks at' the way in which atoms combine to form molecules, the nature of the forces that keep them so bound, and the way in which the bonds between atoms may be broken and re-made. To do this, the chemist will use large numbers of molecules of the compounds concerned, frequently dispersed in a solution in some way; and from the changes obtained in the chemical make-up of the bulk material used, it is inferred that analogous changes have taken place at the molecular level.

To give you some idea of the sheer number of individual molecules that are likely to be present in a sample of a compound, consider the following example. Chemists use a quantity of measurement called a mole. One mole of a substance is the weight in grammes corresponding to the molecular weight of that substance, and it contains approximately 6×10^{23} molecules. That's 6 multiplied by 10 followed by 23 noughts! Now, the molecular weight may readily be calculated from the formula of the compound. So, for example, sodium chloride (salt), which has the formula $NaCl$, has a molecular weight of 58.5, the atomic weights of sodium and chlorine being 23 and 35.5 respectively. This means that 58.5 grammes of salt comprise one mole of this substance. When you sprinkle salt on your food, you are likely to sprinkle on at least a tenth of a gramme or so; let's say, a six-hundredth of a mole. You

have therefore sprinkled approximately 10,000,000,000,000,000,000,000
– ten thousand million million million – molecules of salt on your din-
ner!

Chemists tend to use fairly straightforward apparatus to do their
experiments – glass beakers, flasks and so on, in which they mix their
samples. They may need more complex apparatus to investigate compounds
which are unstable in air; a vacuum or an inert atmosphere are therefore
necessary; and they may use complex machines, which generate characteristic 'spectra' of their compounds (by irradiating them in particular ways,
and plotting the wavelengths of radiation which they absorb), in order to
identify them.

The molecules investigated by chemists may still not be seen directly,
but imaging techniques involving, for example, electron microscopy and
X-ray diffraction can be used to build up pictures of those molecules *in
situ* in a sample of the compound under investigation. Biochemists and
geneticists investigate the behaviour of relatively large, complex, organic
molecules, like proteins, lipids and DNA (an 'organic' molecule, you will
recall, means one which is based on carbon). Again, imaging techniques
mean that these entities may be seen by the eye of the experimenter, if
so desired. Machines may also be used by scientists operating in this
area, for example in the 'sequencing' of proteins and DNA (that is to
say, in carefully breaking them down into the smaller molecules which
constitute them – amino acids in the case of proteins, nucleotides in the
case of DNA – in order to determine the order in which those smaller
molecules are assembled).

The word 'biology' seems to me to cover a vast array of sciences,
but basically biologists look at the behaviour of living systems. These
may be simply single-celled amoebas and the like, which are observed
through microscopes, or they may be much larger organisms: plants,
or animals and humans. The biologist attempts to determine something
of how the parts of such systems work together. A physiologist, for
example, might be interested in how the introduction of a drug to a
living organism affects it; an anatomist might be interested in how
the organs in a living body interact with each other; a neurologist
will be interested in the interactions of drugs and other elements of a
living system with the brain that is a part of it; whilst an evolutionary biologist will be interested in observing the mutations of rapidly
reproducing species in order to try to find out how environmental
and other pressures can lead to changes in the physical make-up of
that species.

Psychologists, sociobiologists and social scientists study the behaviour of individuals and of groups of individuals in order to try to form theories about any general tendencies that there may be in their behaviour. Such scientists will use observations of behaviour under natural or possibly under specially created laboratory conditions to achieve their results. For example, the behaviour of chimpanzees has been extensively studied, both in the wild (in order to understand something of their social behaviour) and in captivity (where experiments have been devised to try to understand the way in which they learn, and what limitations there are in the things that it is possible for them to learn).

There is also an important group of sciences that analyse one-off sources of information rather than performing repeatable experiments – sciences such as archaeology and palaeontology, for example. Here, the sources used by scientists are 'finds' – preserved artefacts, remains, and fossils – and the limited data which may be derived from these are used to attempt to piece together information about the past. Detailed analysis of this data is usually only possible to a limited extent, and much of the practice of these sciences will depend on comparisons of new finds with already existing ones in order to try to establish recognizable patterns. For example, fossil finds are compared with other fossils in order to establish evolutionary trends, and in order to date the rocks which contain them. It is perhaps more appropriate, therefore, to describe these sciences as descriptive or comparative, rather than analytical.

We can therefore see that scientists use a vast array of different techniques, and quite possibly machinery appropriate to those techniques, in order to approach the hugely varied types of material that are considered to be legitimate ground for scientific investigation. Scientists may think in different ways, and operate at different levels, as is most fitting for the particular thing they have decided to study – a sub-atomic particle, or an atom, or an inanimate molecule, up to living organisms of the complexity of human beings, and the operation of large numbers of those organisms together. The sources of scientific information may be any of the above; and indeed, any physical entity is potentially the source of scientific investigation. If it hasn't yet been, it may simply be necessary to devise a new technique or a new paradigm within which to investigate it, or perhaps new machinery with which to do so. Given the source material of a particular science, the worker in that discipline will then apply the appropriate current theories to the data at his or her disposal, using rational thinking to approach the particular problem at hand whenever this is possible. In this use of theory and reason, the sciences all share a common methodology.

The sources used by theology

I commented earlier that the principal sources used by theologians are written ones, and this might be thought to imply that theology operates largely within a 'closed' rather than an 'open' system. This is true when we are considering theology as an intellectual exercise, involving the interpretation and analysis of those written sources. This sort of approach, using our intellects to discover information about God, is sometimes known as 'Natural Theology'.[1] It is likely that theologians of this sort will be in touch with contemporary movements in philosophy and, indeed, in the sciences, which are going on outside the Church, and will bring insights from these areas to bear on their studies. The written sources used by these theologians may appear more limited than the sources used by scientists: in actual fact, considerable variety occurs within them, as we shall shortly see. In their pursuit of their studies, though, it is surely the case that theologians and scientists alike are limited only by the capacities of the intellect itself.

Before proceeding to look in more detail at the sources used by theologians, we should note that the whole idea of natural theology has been subject to considerable criticism on theoretical grounds. It has been urged that since God cannot be known by us solely through the exercise of our intellects and our senses, we are dependent for true knowledge of God on what he has chosen to reveal of himself to us. This leads to the approach known as 'Revealed Theology', which takes as its starting-point the proposition that the only proper sources of information and understanding about God are those which have been revealed as such by God himself. In Christian theology, the principal source of revelation is of course held to be the Bible. Prominent amongst critics of natural theology is the twentieth-century Swiss theologian Karl Barth, who has strongly maintained that our unaided intellects alone are inadequate to the task of understanding anything of God: for such knowledge we must rely totally on what God chooses to reveal to us. Natural theology is, therefore, regarded by Barth as by and large a mistaken enterprise.

These sorts of arguments have considerable force. If God is infinite, and if his fulness is therefore totally beyond our capacity for understanding, it makes some sense to maintain that we may only gain understanding of him through his communication of himself to us, through the medium of revelation: a 'top-down' process, as it were, from God to humankind. 'Bottom-up' approaches, starting from our own understandings of God and the universe, and using our necessarily limited intellectual powers, are always going to be deficient. However, I would maintain that if theology is to be in any sense a public discipline – a subject that people are able to speak to one another about – then we must ultimately base that public discourse on our experiences, and on our interpretations of those experiences. In other words, for theology actually to take place our experiences and understandings of revelation must be vocalised, and hence our intellects must necessarily have a part to play in our coming to any collective (as opposed to purely personal) understanding of God. The story is told of the great medieval scholar and Saint, St Thomas Aquinas, who wrote at considerable length about theological issues, that towards the end of his life he received a vision of God. After this he wrote no more, saying that all he had written up to that time now seemed like so much straw.[2] Barth's understanding of theology would suggest that it was in his private silence rather than in his public writings that St Thomas was being the more authentic theologian. This may be perfectly true, but it does not contribute much to the furthering of theological endeavour in generally accessible, public terms.

Having noted Barth's objections, then, I shall continue to think of theology as first and foremost an intellectual exercise operating upon source material. What are the sources available to us for use in theological investigations?

In the same way that the physical universe, the field of study of the sciences, is actually an immense entity which we do not attempt to comprehend in its entirety through any particular experiment, but which we approach piecemeal through the different models provided by the different scientific disciplines – each one of them giving us (we believe) an understanding of an aspect of the universe – so, too, God, the field of study of theology, is generally agreed to be an immense entity or concept, approachable only through our studying different aspects of his immensity at any one time. Moreover, each of our various investigations will give us a different insight into the enormousness of God.

In the same way that there are many sources used by scientists, it may be observed that there are many sources used by theologians. The written sources used by them include the Bible, commentaries on the Bible by past scholars, and more speculative theological writings that take the Bible as a starting-point and then develop its teachings in one direction or another. One way in which the grounds of Christian belief have been characterized is in terms of the three-fold basis of Scripture, tradition and reason, and I want now to use this model as a framework within which to discuss theological sources. Scripture, the Bible, is the primary source of information about the Christian God: all theology takes it as its starting-point. The tradition of the Christian Church is summarized in creeds, in formal doctrines, and in the writings of past generations of believers about their experiences in their quest for a greater understanding of God. The importance of this tradition has been variously emphasized by the different Christian denominations, but it is safe to say that absolutely all Christians tap into some aspect of it, whether they consciously acknowledge the fact or not. It is obviously important too that theologians should use the faculty of reason which we all possess, in order to remain self-consistent, and in order to relate their reflections to the wider wisdom of the secular age in which they are working. After all, if God is the source and origin of the world and all that is in it, then all human wisdom is ultimately attributable to him, and it is therefore highly appropriate to use reason in our pursuit of a greater understanding of him.

Let us now examine these three bases of theology in greater detail for the light they shed on the sources used by theology.

The Bible

The first point that needs to be made about the Bible is that it is not a book. It is, rather, a collection of books, written over a period of anything up to 1000 years, and incorporating material that may have been circulating for some time in an oral form before it was first written down. These books of the Bible may be approached in very many different ways: as literary texts, as devotional writings praising God or pouring out feelings to him, as historical narratives, and so on.

We must also recognize that the books of the Bible are written in many different styles, since their assorted writers were attempting to say many different things to their readers. When approaching a biblical book, it is important for us to try to understand, as far as we are able, the type of writing involved (the *genre* of the book), and thus to try to make the way in which we read that book relevant to the text in question. For example, the books of Chronicles were intended to present the history of Israel, albeit from a particular perspective. We will therefore find in these books only casual, incidental glimpses of the contemporary Jewish understandings of the character of God, and so we should not be reading them in the hope of finding out very much about this aspect of Jewish religious life. The book of Daniel appears to have been written to provide moral and spiritual support for Jews during a time of persecution in the second century BCE: it is therefore a mistake to view it as providing a literal account of the exploits of Jewish captives in Babylon some four centuries previously, which is when the 'narrative' of the book is set (although, of course, it *may* conceivably contain older material relevant to such an account). The bizarre images and complex symbolism of the book of Daniel belong to a tradition of writing called *apocalyptic* literature: the book of Revelation at the very end of the Bible is a later example of this sort of literary genre. Much speculative ink has been expended in producing attempts at interpreting such extraordinary books as these: however, any attempts that fail to set this literature squarely in the time of its original composition are surely bound to misfire in their understanding of it.

In addition to such material, we have in the Old Testament texts which are, in effect, hymns (the Psalms); books which fall into the category of Wisdom literature, exploring such age-old problems as the nature of suffering and of happiness, or containing aphorisms which are intended to convey moral wisdom (Job, Proverbs, Ecclesiastes and the like); and books setting out ritual Jewish laws and telling the story, part history, part myth, of the origins of mankind in general and of the people of Israel in particular (the first five books of the Bible, commonly referred to as the Pentateuch). In the New Testament we have books telling the story of Jesus' life, and inviting their readers to believe in him as the Son of God (the Gospels); and letters from Christian religious leaders, offering practical advice and theological reflections on all sorts of matters (the New Testament Epistles). And there are many other books in the Bible besides these. So although the Bible might appear to be rather a monolithic thing – a single book – it is in fact a library of different texts, saying a variety of different things about God, and about what it means to be a human being standing in relation to God, from their authors' various different historical and social perspectives. In the next chapter we shall be looking at the critical tools that theologians have developed in order to study the books of the Bible more effectively, and to analyse such issues as how those books came to be written in the first place, and to what extent their authors wrote freely or adapted texts that already existed. For now, though, let us simply confine ourselves to noting that the Bible is an incredibly rich and diverse source of centuries-old wisdom regarding the nature of God, as he has been understood by people in the past. We might therefore say that the Bible, properly treated, can be regarded in its own way as a source almost of comparable richness and variety to the sources used by the natural sciences.

Not only was the Bible *written* in a variety of different ways, to serve a variety of different purposes in the past: it should also be *read* in a variety of different ways by us today, depending on the different genres of the books it contains. It is foolish to try to read texts recounting myths as history, as it is foolish to try to read texts which are hymns of praise in search of a weather forecast. To be sure, the book of Genesis depicts God as making the world in six days, and resting on the seventh; but since the evidence available to us today is far in excess of that available to the writer of the book of Genesis, and our understanding of the physical world is so much greater, we may surely say that the importance of this story lies not so much in its literal as in its symbolic truth – in the idea it expresses of God as Creator. (One might indeed question the extent to which its author(s) actually intended it to be expressing a literal truth in the first place.) Similarly, Psalm 104 speaks of God making the clouds his chariot, and riding upon the wings of the wind: but does this meteorological image mean that such weather conditions infallibly indicate the physical presence of God? Of course not: an image like this is not one that we should take literally (again, I suspect that it may not even have been taken literally in ancient Israel, when it was written). Its truth, surely, lies in the poetic image it presents of God: of God, mighty and powerful as the winds, and unpredictable as the weather. It is our obsession with literalness that is responsible for such misreadings as these. The Genesis account of creation is not history, and the Psalms are not weather forecasting.

If we are to approach the Bible in search of information about God we will (not surprisingly) find very different portrayals of God in the different types of literature the Bible contains. Here are a few examples, which will I hope serve to illustrate the way in which people's understandings of God change within the Bible itself. (I should add that the account that follows is greatly simplified: it presents a general outline only. The full story of how ideas about God have developed in the Bible is far more complicated than that presented here.)

Early ideas about God in the Old Testament appear to see him as little more than the tribal God of the nation of Israel. God is even sometimes referred to in ways that make it appear that he is one among many gods. For example, Psalm 77. 13 reads, 'Your way O God is holy. Who is so great a God as our God?'; and, even more remarkably, Psalm 82 begins with the declaration, 'God has stood up in the council of heaven: in the midst of the gods he gives judgment.' This is the God who aided the people of Israel in their liberation from slavery in Egypt, who went ahead of them as fire and cloud during their wanderings in the wilderness, and who aided them in driving out and killing the inhabitants of the Promised Land. God spoke directly to Moses, from out of a burning bush and subsequently on Mount Sinai (stories found in the book of Exodus: see Exodus 3. 1 ff. and 19. 20 ff.). Moses was the greatest of all the prophets, 'whom the Lord knew face to face' (Deuteronomy 34. 10); and God gave laws for the nation of Israel to Moses, including the command that there should be no attempt to make images of God (Exodus 20. 4).

Later, God appears to be considered as quite literally living in the midst of the people, in the Temple at Jerusalem. Psalm 48. 3 reads, 'On Mount Zion where godhead truly dwells stands the city of the Great King: God is well known in her palaces as a sure defence', and in Psalm 76 we read that 'At Salem is [God's] tabernacle, and his dwelling is in Zion' (verse 2).

God appears in the writings of some of the earlier prophets as an angry God, a God who demands justice and moral uprightness from his people and who threatens them with destruction if they do not listen to him. This aspect of God may be seen in the book of Amos, for example:

Hear this, you that trample upon the needy,
and bring to ruin the poor of the land,
saying, 'When will the new moon be over,
so that we may sell grain;
and the Sabbath, so that we may offer wheat
  for sale?
We will . . . practise deceit with false balances,
buying the poor for silver,
and the needy for a pair of sandals,
and selling the sweepings of the wheat.'
The Lord has sworn by the pride of Jacob:
Surely I will never forget any of their deeds.
Shall not the land tremble on this account,
and everyone mourn who lives in it?

(Amos 8. 4–8)

So much for religion not getting mixed up with politics!

Then the unthinkable happened: the destruction threatened by some of these prophets actually came about. In about the year 587 BCE Jerusalem was captured, and the leaders of the Jewish nation were deported to Babylon. This crushing and bewildering blow to the Jewish people is reflected in Psalms commenting on the destruction they have witnessed – Psalms clearly written by people stunned at what had happened:

Your adversaries have made uproar in the place
  appointed for your praise:
They have set up their standards in triumph.
They have destroyed on every side,
like those who take axes up to a thicket of trees.
All the carved woodwork they have broken down,
and smashed it with hammers and hatchets.
They have set fire to your sanctuary,
and defiled to the ground the dwelling-place
  of your name.

(Psalm 74. 4–7)

How could God have let such things happen?

> O God, the heathen have come into your land.
> They have defiled your holy Temple:
> they have made Jerusalem a heap of stones.
> They have given the dead bodies of your servants
> as food to the birds of the air . . .
> How long, O Lord, shall your anger be so extreme?
>
> (Psalm 79. 1–2, 5)

The misery of the exiles' plight in their captivity is captured vividly in the famous opening of Psalm 137: 'By the waters of Babylon we sat down and wept, when we remembered Zion.'

However, there in Babylon a new, and very beautiful, insight into the nature of God was to emerge: the understanding of God as the comforter of his people, the one who forgives them their past sins. This new voice is found in our book of Isaiah, though it seems impossible that the historical figure of the prophet Isaiah, who lived much earlier, could be responsible for it:

> Comfort, O comfort my people, says your God.
> Speak tenderly to Jerusalem, and cry to her
> that she has served her term, that her penalty is
>   paid.
>
> (Isaiah 40. 1–2)

Later still comes the idea that God is the God of *all* the nations, not just of the people of Israel. This is illustrated by the story of Jonah, who was sent by God to Nineveh, the capital city of the Assyrians, to preach against the people there. When those people turned away from their sins, God forgave them – much to Jonah's chagrin! A further new dimension is introduced by the book of Daniel, which, as has been mentioned, is an example of the genre of apocalyptic writing. This book portrays God as 'An ancient one', seated on a heavenly (that is, other-worldly) throne, dressed in white and with hair 'Like pure wool' (Daniel 7. 9 ff.). The contrast to earlier understandings of God could not, it appears, be greater. Instead of the God who may not be pictured, dwelling in the midst of his people, we have God being represented in the form of a human being, and dwelling not within this world, but rather somewhere beyond it.

Still further developments in the human understanding of God are to be found in the New Testament, principally of course those which are found in the person and teaching of Jesus. Earlier Jewish understandings of God had suggested either that he was an immanent God (dwelling, in some sense, with his people), or that he was a transcendent God (removed from the world, and in some sense high above it, as in the book of Daniel). Jesus presented his hearers with a novel understanding of God which showed God to be both immanent *and* transcendent, simultaneously. We may see this complex idea presented with extraordinary simplicity in the opening line of the Lord's Prayer: 'Our Father in heaven' (Matthew 6. 9). The use of the word 'Father' by Jesus appears to be a characteristic way in which he understood his relationship to God, and Christians have followed him in addressing God in this way: thus God is seen as being close to, even intimate with, the one who prays this prayer. He is an immanent God, given the name 'God is with us' (Matthew 1. 23, quoting Isaiah 7. 14). However, God also remains simultaneously 'in heaven' – that is to say, transcendent – in terms of his relation to the world.

The idea that 'God is love' is also a New Testament idea, which may be found in the first letter of John (1 John 4. 16). This represents in effect an abstraction of the idea of God away from the more personal (and, not infrequently, more anthropomorphic) understandings of God that characterize many of the earlier biblical books. This use of abstraction in thinking about God was a way that was to be followed a great deal more in future centuries.

Here, then, are some understandings of God that may be found in the pages of the Bible. Let us now turn to the Christian tradition as a source of material for theological inquiry.

Christian tradition

Tradition has been important right from the earliest days of the Christian Church. The Christian understanding of God continued to grow beyond the New Testament period, taking on or developing further abstract ideas about God, such as for example the ideas that God is all-good, all-powerful and so on. Much of this understanding of God was in fact derived from contemporary neo-Platonic philosophy, at that time the most widespread and highly regarded kind of theistic philosophy, and so naturally the one to which early Christian thinkers turned in their efforts to 'unpack' the meanings of the biblical writings.[3] Doctrines such as that of the Holy Trinity, and that of the understanding of Christ's nature as both fully human and fully divine, likewise come from the early Christian centuries, and are the result of the greatest theological thinkers of those years attempting to grapple with practical puzzles about God in terms of the most advanced philosophical thinking of their age. That tradition of understanding has been added to down the centuries by scores of theologians and thinkers of all descriptions, and continues to be added to and interpreted afresh by the Church in each generation.

The great spiritual traditions within the Church represent precisely this sort of elaboration of Christian ideas, elaborations that have been tried and tested through centuries of experience. By way of examples, I should like to consider three highly influential spiritual traditions of the past that remain sources of inspiration for people to this day: early monasticism, Franciscan spirituality, and the writings of St John of the Cross. (Of course, these are only a few of the many different forms of spiritual expression that have been found helpful by Christians down the centuries.) They are quite wide-ranging in their emphases, and this is surely only appropriate. Since each of us has his or her own unique psychological make-up, then we will each respond differently to different stimuli, be those stimuli physical, aesthetic, spiritual, or whatever. Yet it is surely the case that the traditions which I am about to describe would not have survived to today if they had not been found to be of enduring value to Christians of different ages.

Monasticism – the living of one's life according to a rule, which generally hinges around sexual chastity, renunciation of possessions, regular and frequent worship of God, manual labour of some sort, and obedience to a superior – may be traced back to the early Christians who were known as the Desert Fathers (although this group in fact included both men and women). The most famous of these early ascetics was St Antony of Egypt, who, at the age of about twenty, sold all his possessions and went to live in the company of others who were practising an ascetic regime. During the years 286 to 306 CE he lived in complete solitude in the desert. Other men, and women too, followed his example and went out into desert regions of Egypt and the Middle East, either as individuals or as members of more or less tightly knit communities, in order to remove themselves from normal human society and devote themselves to prayer and devotion. Their ascetic exercises, many of which strike the modern reader as somewhat excessive, and which have led one writer to dub them 'solitary Christian over-achievers',[4] went all the way from eating very plain diets and dressing very simply, to living, in a few celebrated cases, on the top of stone pillars up to twelve metres high. Yet these men and women gained great reputations for wisdom, and were frequently sought out by fellow Christians who were looking for guidance. They left no writings, but various collections of their sayings and deeds were made, and have come down to us. They reveal a simple, even naïve, kind of wisdom; but it is a wisdom born of considerable humility. The following anecdote, concerning St Antony himself, is typical:

One day some old men came to see Father Antony. In the midst of them was Father Joseph. Wanting to test them, the old man suggested a text from the Scriptures, and, beginning with the youngest, he asked them what it meant. Each gave his opinion as he was able. But to each one the old man said, 'You have not understood it.' Last of all he said to Father Joseph, 'How would you explain this saying?' and he replied, 'I do not know.' Then Father Antony said, 'Indeed, Father Joseph has found the way, for he has said: "I do not know." '[5]

Later monastic visions owe a great deal to the Desert Fathers. The various monastic rules that came to be established – Augustinian, Benedictine, and others – though operating in a more systematic way, still pursued the same sort of ideals as those of the early monks and hermits of the desert.

St Francis of Assisi was born in 1181 or 1182 into a wealthy family. He renounced his worldly wealth, as many of the Desert Fathers had before him, and devoted himself to proclaiming peace, poverty and brotherhood. For him, the first two of these were intertwined: without possessions we have no need of weapons to defend them, and so poverty makes people instruments of God's peace. All things were called 'brother' and 'sister' by St Francis: he even described the stars as his sisters. This perception of the relatedness of all things, and, in particular, of our own relatedness to the whole of creation, characterizes his thinking. In fact, he saw the human condition as being all about relationships – relationships with each other, with the world, and, most importantly of course, with God. St Francis' beautiful 'Canticle of the Sun' invokes the whole of creation in an act of worshipping God. Its stanzas begin with the following lines:

Praised be you, my Lord, with all your creatures,
    especially Brother Sun . . .
Praised be you, my Lord, through Sister Moon
    and the stars . . .
Praised be you, my Lord, through Brother Wind . . .
Praised be you, my Lord, through Sister Water . . .
Praised be you, my Lord, through Brother Fire . . .
Praised be you, my Lord, through our Sister,
    Mother Earth . . .[6]

This way of thinking has obvious parallels with ecological movements in the twentieth-century world. St Francis' followers, now organized in the order called the Franciscans, continue to promote his ideals in the way he did – by proclaiming them both by what they preach and by what they do.

St John of the Cross was a sixteenth-century Spanish Carmelite friar, active, along with his friend St Teresa of Avila, in renewing that religious order. He is remembered especially for his poetry, which tells of the pain and joy involved in the progression of the soul towards union with God in Christ. His poems introduce the idea of 'The Dark Night of the Soul', drawing an analogy between drawing closer to God through meditation and passing through night. This journey towards God begins with the night of the senses, as the senses are left behind as the Self concentrates more and more on God; and the darkest part of this night is the night of the Spirit, as the Self is stripped of its all, its everything, every last consolation and element of self-understanding. Only beyond this can the soul finally break into the day, the illumination of union with God. God is seen as the one in whom all our humanity is stripped away as we draw near to him; and our humanity is seen as that which is in fact designed to be so stripped. I find it difficult enough simply to write about St John of the Cross's poetry: the task of setting down spiritual experiences, as that poetry does, is totally beyond my capacity, and I can only recommend that interested readers pursue such matters further by reading St John's poems themselves.[7]

Seeking after God in utter simplicity and self-discipline (the Desert Fathers): seeking after God through seeing oneself as a part of the whole of creation, and as intimately related to it (St Francis of Assisi): pursuing union with God through the total abnegation of self (St John of the Cross). Three very different approaches to that phenomenon that we term the spiritual, all of which have been, and still are, found useful by Christians, and each of which forms an important part of the spiritual tradition of the Church. All these insights, then, together with those of many other spiritual thinkers, form a resource which may be used in the pursuit of theological investigations.

Reason

Although the principal sources of Christian theology have always been the Bible and the writings of the great theologians of the past, it has also long been recognized that the human faculty of reason must have a part to play in theological development. An element of interpretation will always be necessary when we read texts such as these, if we wish to derive information from them. The Bible, for example, is far from unambiguous, and can bear many interpretations. This was recognized as long ago as the fourth century CE by St Augustine, who wrote:

Consider what scripture offers and what its language expresses in a single phrase: 'In the beginning God made heaven and earth'. Cannot this bear many interpretations, not including misleading errors, but true interpretations of different kinds?[8]

Reason is obviously the most appropriate tool to use for such a task of interpretation.

In addition to these literary sources for theology, it has been suggested that the physical world itself can tell us something of God. Since the universe is God's creation, we might, with some reason, expect to be able to find out information about God from it. This approach is at least as old as the Psalms, where it is given poetic expression thus: 'The heavens declare the glory of God, and the firmament proclaims his handiwork' (Psalm 19. 1) – a sentiment familiar to many through Haydn's chorus 'The heavens are telling' in his oratorio 'The Creation'. It has often been observed in past centuries that the universe is both very beautiful, and very ordered; and it has correspondingly been inferred that God is a God of both beauty and order. Our own century, which has perhaps seen more than any previous era of the appallingly destructive behaviour of which human beings are capable, and has correspondingly witnessed suffering on a previously unimagined scale, is perhaps rightly rather sceptical about this sort of approach, and has focused considerable attention on the so-called 'problem of evil'. If God is all-good, all-knowing, and all-powerful (so the argument runs), then how is it that we witness so much evil and suffering in the world? The presence of this evil surely suggests either that God permits it (in which case, how can he be all-good?), or that he is unaware of it (in which case, how can he be all-knowing?), or that he can't do anything about it (in which case, how can he be all-powerful?). So – should the world be seen as a beautifully ordered creation of God, revealing to us by its very nature something of God himself? Or if it is rather a place in which dreadful evils can occur, why doesn't God do something about it? These related issues are extremely complex, and can only be touched on rather than addressed with the fullness they deserve in the context of this book. I shall, however, deal briefly with them in a diversion at the end of this chapter.

Of course, the approach which suggests that we may perceive God in the natural world can be taken to extremes. One such extreme is that known as pantheism, which is the idea that God is literally present throughout all of nature, and that in fact God and the natural world are to all intents and purposes indistinguishable. Modern emphases on holistic approaches to the universe and the place of humankind within it might appear to encourage this kind of approach, and it has also been developed by some Christian mystics (such as Meister Eckhart) who wished to stress the unity of all things in God.[9] More recently, as we have seen, theologians have developed the model of the universe as the Body of God. It cannot be denied that this model yields fascinating insights into God and his relationship with the universe, fascinating particularly in this latter part of the twentieth century when ecological issues must inevitably feature prominently on the agenda of any theologian who interacts with the secular world.

However, pantheism has in general found little favour with orthodox theologians. It blurs entirely the distinction between the Creator and the created, and in emphasizing the immanence of God in creation does not provide any means of accounting for his transcendence over it: in other words, it fails to shed any light on God's 'otherness' to the natural world. Of rather greater appeal to the more orthodox mind, perhaps, is the idea known as pan*en*theism, which suggests that all the universe is contained by God, but that there are aspects of God which lie outside the physical universe.

It might well be argued that panentheism provides an account of the relationship between God and the physical world that is better than that of pantheism, in that it sits well alongside more traditional and orthodox ideas about that relationship. The incarnation of Christ is sometimes referred to as a 'self-emptying' of God (the Greek word is *kenosis*), following the idea expressed in the biblical letter to the Philippians: 'Christ Jesus . . . emptied himself, taking the form of a servant' (Philippians 2. 7). In the same way, the universe might perhaps be thought of in terms of its being the overflowing bounty of God, 'godliness', as it were, that God's superabundant nature was no longer able to contain, and which was therefore emptied out of himself. The universe is therefore in some sense contained within God, whence it originated, but God remains more than it.

Another issue arising from the orderliness of the universe, as mentioned above, is that this orderliness has often been held to point to its having had a creator. This is the basis of the so-called 'Argument from Design' for the existence of God: the order which we can see in the cosmos points to it having been designed to be the way it is, and if that is the case, then the designer of the cosmos must exist. But, it might be urged, isn't all that a bit old hat? Hasn't science done away with such a view, with its understanding of the physical world and how it came into being?

In one sense, the answer to that question is certainly, Yes. The creation stories found in the opening chapters of Genesis are demonstrably not literally true. However, if these stories are taken as indicating that God is in some sense a creator God – a God who ordered creation from out of nothing, the stories themselves illustrating poetically the creation process

– then this picture of God is perhaps not so incompatible with modern science after all. One of the most remarkable things that recent scientific advances in our understanding of the physical universe have shown is that it is, above all things, ordered – and ordered, moreover, with quite incredible accuracy. Life as we know it could not have come about in any old universe: for it to have arisen at all requires the universe which contains it to be very, very similar indeed, in terms of the physical laws which obtain in it, to the one in which we do in fact find ourselves. This observation forms the basis of what has become known as the anthropic principle, which has been stated in a variety of ways, but which may be summarized in one of its expressions as the notion that our universe *must* be the way it is in order for us to be present in it to observe it. Just how ordered the universe is, and what conclusions we may draw on the basis of its orderliness, I shall examine in the diversion at the end of this chapter.

Calculations which have to be based in a large measure on assumptions and guesswork should be treated with a certain scepticism. Nevertheless, for the sake of interest we may note that one estimate of the odds against the universe we live in having come about by chance puts those odds at one in one followed by a thousand billion billion zeros – a truly unimaginable figure! (Compare it with the figure on page 62, which looks like a pretty large figure itself, but which is actually only one followed by 22 zeros!) Now, the 'argument from design' used to be seen as a powerful argument for the existence of God; and whilst such observations as this do not in any way provide a watertight demonstration of God's existence, yet they provide a certain basis for thinking that the universe might not have come about purely by chance, but through the mediation of a creator, however that creator may be imagined. It appears in this instance that our understanding of the natural world in the light of modern science may play a part in our being enabled to broaden our ideas about God.

To summarize the argument of this chapter so far: theologians have a variety of sources at their disposal when attempting to approach God, the subject of their investigations. We have emphasized that the Bible is best regarded as a library of books, rather than as just a single one. There is a great variety of models of God to be derived both from the biblical authors and from post-biblical authors from within the Christian tradition; and much may be learned from setting these texts in their historical periods and examining the genres of the writings involved. This may in turn help to establish the way in which the books in question were intended by their authors to be read. The theologian can also bring to bear the faculty of reason on his or her subject matter; and inferences about God may in addition be made from our observations of the physical world, if this world is assumed to be in some sense God's creation. The theologian wishing to understand more about God is thus faced with a huge diversity of sources affording different insights and different information. In the same sort of way, the scientist gleans different sorts of information about the physical world from the different source material available to him or her from the different scientific disciplines, and also operates upon them, in the framework provided by current theories, by his or her reason. In both cases, there are a variety of sources to be used, enabling a variety of approaches to be taken to those sources. In both cases, traditions of interpretation of the source material (theological traditions or scientific theories) are applied to the source material. In both cases, it is expected that the discourse be predominantly a rational one. Finally, I would suggest that in both cases a prevailing orthodoxy suggests which approaches adopted by the theologian or the scientist are to be considered legitimate and which are not. This point needs to be discussed further.

Orthodoxy

What are these orthodoxies? A current scientific orthodoxy, of course, is simply the paradigm that we mentioned earlier. This paradigm can change (albeit sometimes reluctantly) and establish a new orthodoxy when new data becomes available. Theological orthodoxy is apparently a rather more monolithic thing, and major changes in orthodoxy occur seldom (and possibly with considerable upheaval, if past instances such as the Reformation are anything to go by). However, within that prevailing orthodoxy, considerable breadth of thought is generally possible. Given the variety of understandings of God that are reflected upon in the pages of the Bible, there is a fair chance that the individual believer may arrive at an understanding of God, derived from Scripture, tradition and reason, which he or she finds accessible, whilst remaining perfectly orthodox. It might of course be asked why orthodoxy is so important that such efforts should be made for its preservation. I shall examine this question, and the question of how changes to a prevailing orthodoxy can in fact come about, in Chapter 7.

Changes in the ways in which we think about God have undoubtedly taken place since the Bible was written. As examples of this, consider the doctrines of the Trinity and of the dual nature of Christ, both of which were developed within the early Church. More recent thinkers have come up with ideas about God based on the Bible which they felt were more in accord with the prevailing understanding of human beings of their day. It is surely only to be expected that human understandings of God can – indeed, must – change with the changes in other aspects of our understandings of ourselves and our universe.

It has also been suggested that God himself is in a state of evolution along with the universe: in other words, that God himself is constantly changing. This is a point which is emphasized by the school of thought known as Process Theology. Like most 'schools', this term in fact encompasses a variety of different approaches, though it is generally held to be based on the kind of thinking developed by A. N. Whitehead and Charles Hartshorne. It has been described as 'Theology which emphasises event, becoming and relatedness as basic categories for understanding rather than those of substance and being'[10] – in other words, God, the universe and all that is within the universe are regarded in terms of their being in a dynamic state of 'becoming' rather than in a static state of simply 'being'. It is surely the case that this sort of theological thinking ties in very well with the scientific understandings of the universe and life on our planet being subject to the processes of evolution, since evolution is, at bottom, a process of becoming. Here once again, then, we see the potential for scientific and theological understandings about the cosmos and the condition of human beings within it gaining insights from one another.

A word about method

We have already noted that there are similarities between science and theology in terms of what they finally generate: a form of understanding that is based in each case partly upon knowledge and partly upon belief. In this chapter, we have seen that although science and theology look to very different sources, yet in each case the sources used are many in number, and the sorts of thinking used in each of the disciplines have many parallels. We might say that whilst the data-collection parts of these disciplines operate in very different areas, the data-analysis parts may be more alike than otherwise. When it comes to examining the 'raw material' of each discipline, and of forming theories based on that raw material, scientists and theologians alike may employ similar methods. Each will try to proceed in more or less logical and rational ways in analysing the data at his or her disposal: each will try to devise simple theories which explain all the data which it is desired to explain, rather than complicated ones. In general, both scientists and theologians seek to derive, from a consideration of all the data that is available to them, the best available explanation for those data.

It might be said that theologians are in general rather more willing than scientists to admit the importance of the free exercising of our imaginations in pursuing their studies. However, we have seen that science can proceed through the use of imagination, both in terms of the formation of new theories and in terms of speculations aimed at solving specific problems. For example, the discovery of the structure of the benzene molecule, referred to in Chapter 2, came about through the exercise of Kekulé's imagination. Scientists also sometimes make use of what are called 'thought experiments'. In these, an experiment is devised which it would be impossible, or at least extremely difficult, to bring about in a practical context, and the possible consequences of that experiment are explored using the imagination. It might be urged that such 'experimentation' belongs more to the worlds of theology or philosophy or even literature, in which imaginative speculation might be thought to play a more important part. In fact, thought experiments can play a very useful role in the development of the sciences, particularly in the teaching context. There is room, then, in both the sciences and in theology, for the use of the imagination in speculative attempts at problem-solving; and perhaps scientists could learn from the example of theologians in using their imaginations a little more freely.

To conclude this section, let us note that theology and science alike use a plurality of sources, and process the information they derive from them in analogous ways. We may also note that, in addition to the many similarities we have observed, it also makes sense to speak of a certain complementarity between these two disciplines. It is virtually impossible to construct a total world-view based solely on either the physical sciences or on theological principles derived from the Bible.[11] If the challenge to scientist and religious believer alike is to construct such a world-view, which adequately explains absolutely every aspect of human experience as fully as possible, then (I would maintain) each needs to be aided by the expertise of the other.

Stannard has expressed the complementarity of science and theology thus: '[Scientific discussion] deals only with how-type questions, i.e. how things behave; it does not deal with why-type questions – those to do with purpose.'[12] It is questions regarding purpose and meaning that are, by and large, the preserve of the theologian. It is noteworthy that when theology addresses how-type questions and science addresses why-type questions, the results tend to be equally facile. Using theological insight alone, we might answer the question 'How does the world come to be as it is?' by saying, 'God made it that way.' Using science alone, we might answer the question 'What is the purpose of human existence?' by saying, 'There isn't one.' Both these answers are consistent with the systems of thinking which generate them, although there is far more that can be said in answering both these questions if we look outside those systems, to insights from others.

In general, we might say that in some purely mathematical areas, theology might not have a lot to say: in some purely spiritual areas, science might not have a lot to say. However, most of the questions that we wish to ask are not about one of these areas, but rather about issues somewhere on a scale running between them. In facing such complex questions, insights from both science *and* theology, taken together, can usually paint a broader picture than an account derived from one discipline alone. I believe that the sources and ideas of the sciences and of theology are best regarded in this way: as complementary to one another, rather than as mutually incompatible. Both are of enormous value if we wish to pursue to the full the quest for a greater understanding of ourselves and of our universe.

Diversion: the anthropic principle and the problem of evil

A brief diversion cannot possibly begin to come to grips with two subjects as enormous and as complex as these. Nevertheless, I cannot omit a discussion of such important topics altogether, and I hope that even an inadequate treatment of them, such as this account must inevitably be, will be better than nothing.

First, the anthropic principle. As mentioned above, this is basically the idea that the universe must be the way it is in order for us to be present in it to observe it. The anthropic principle has been expressed in a number of different ways, more or less provocative and more or less controversial.[13] Let us now examine some of the scientific observations that led to the formulation of this principle in the first place.

There are four fundamental forces which operate in the physical world: gravity, electromagnetism, the weak nuclear force and the strong nuclear force. Each of these has a particular strength, both in absolute terms and in terms of their ratios one with another. For example, the universal gravitational constant G has a value of 6.672×10^{-11} Nm^{2}kg^{-2}. Any two particles in the universe will attract each other with a force that is equal to G multiplied by each of their masses and divided by the square of the distance between them. The other three fundamental forces likewise have specific values. It turns out that *these forces all need to be very close indeed to their observed values if the universe as we know it is to come about.* Moreover, the ratios between these forces also need to be very close indeed to those ratios which are actually found to be the case. Likewise, the masses of the fundamental particles, and the ratios of those masses, need to be very close to their observed values for our universe to exist at all. In fact, some forces and masses need to be fine-tuned to the values which we observe not for just one, but for several reasons; and as one commentator has remarked, 'Mustn't it be inexplicably good fortune that the requirements which have to be satisfied do not conflict?'[14]

As an example of all this, consider the force of gravity. The universe, it is now well established, is flying apart as though from the impetus of an enormous explosion: this explosion is generally known as the 'big bang'. It turns out that if gravity were to be ever so slightly stronger than it is, then immediately following that initial explosion all the matter produced by it would have been attracted back in upon itself, resulting in a 'big crunch'. On the other hand, if gravity were to be ever so slightly weaker than it is, then the matter produced by the big bang would simply have flown apart with such vigour that it could never have coalesced to produce stars and galaxies. The same thing applies to all the other forces, and to the ratios between them: if they were even slightly different to their observed value, the universe that we know could never have come into existence at all.

Three possibilities follow from this. The first is that the universe was consciously designed to be as it is, somehow and by somebody or something. The second is that, by a remote, quite literally unbelievably small probability, our universe has come into existence purely by chance, possessing, again quite by chance, all the features necessary for life to develop within it. The third is that in fact our universe is actually one of many universes – so many, in fact, that the possibility of one of them being like ours, capable of generating and supporting sentient life within it, becomes high enough to be plausibly attributable to chance.

Clearly, both of the first two possibilities mentioned here involve an enormous step of belief on the part of anyone who wishes to uphold one of them (I would urge, in fact, that belief in God is by far the more realistic belief of the two). But what about the third option – that our universe is in fact only one of many? How could this come about?

Four descriptions of multiple universes have been postulated. First, it has been suggested that universes expand from big bangs and contract in big crunches in a regular, oscillating pattern, with the values of the fundamental forces varying randomly from one oscillation to the next. Our universe is simply one such oscillation, which is extremely long-lived due to the values the forces have assumed within it. Second, it has been suggested that universes may arise at random through quantum fluctuations, and may turn out to be long-lived if their total energy chances to be very small. Third, it has been suggested that every time an event happens at the quantum level, our universe divides in two, in one of which the outcome of the event is one of its possible outcomes and in the other of which it is the other outcome. Remember Schrödinger's cat (Chapter

2)? This suggestion would maintain that two universes were generated as a result of the quantum event at the heart of that experiment, in one of which the cat lived, and in the other of which the cat died. Fourth, it has been suggested that space is in fact 'open'. The universe that we observe has limits to it set by the distance that light can have travelled since the big bang (i.e. about fifteen billion light-years, the universe we observe being, it is estimated, about fifteen billion years old). It is generally assumed that space as well as time originated with the big bang, so that the question 'What is there outside our universe?' is a meaningless one. But what if, beyond the 'horizon' of our universe, there are in fact further universes, our universe being one among many that co-exist in separate space?

Four fascinating ideas, to be sure. However, they are all completely beyond our powers to examine further from a scientific perspective, and must remain therefore entirely speculative. Anyone believing in the existence of a plurality of universes existing alongside our own is leaping well beyond the bounds of science. We might even say that the exercise they are involved in is myth-making – and these are myths which, probably unlike many ancient myths, are completely without any discernible basis in reality.

In short, even this option of there being many universes, of which ours just happens to appear to be the only one because it is the one in which life has evolved and is able to observe it, does not really provide a more reasonable explanation for the extraordinarily 'fine-tuned' nature of our universe than the alternatives suggested earlier. Nor, in any case, would the existence of many universes (if this could in fact be demonstrated) disprove the existence of God. After all, God might in some sense have created them all.

Of course, even if the fine tuning of the universe is admitted as providing evidence for the existence of a God who made the universe, it tells us nothing at all about the nature of that God. Leslie has concluded that all that may be said of the God shown to us by observations such as these is that he is a 'Creatively effective ethical requirement that there be a good Universe or universes'.[15] Perhaps this rather austere description simply serves to illustrate the necessarily limited capabilities of pure natural theology when it comes to speaking about God: our own unaided intellects can only derive this grey and shadowy God flitting around in the background. Richer and more complete understandings of God may only be arrived at through the medium of God's revelation of himself to us, as religious traditions have always maintained, rather than through our attempts to grasp with our finite intellects the infinite nature of God. This is the point where we may see a complementarity between natural theology and revealed theology.

These considerations may also cast some light on the age-old problem of evil. It may seem that we are making a pretty massive leap in doing so at this point, but the reasons for considering this issue here will, I hope, soon become clear. You'll recall that the problem of evil is that of how there can be an all-good, all-knowing, all-powerful God who yet permits the evil that we observe all around us in our world.[16] This is an extremely powerful argument: in fact, it is the one that I encounter most frequently in people I meet who cannot bring themselves to believe in God. It is certainly an argument the force of which I myself feel very acutely when confronted by the immeasurable suffering in our world that assails us regularly in our news bulletins. There are, I think, three basic approaches open to one who wishes to defend the existence of God in the face of such an argument.

The first is far and away the least satisfactory. It is to assert that, whilst we see things from our limited temporal perspectives, God is able to see all of history at one time, since he exists outside time. From this privileged position, which is denied to us, God is able to see that in fact the overall purposes of creation remain good, despite the evil which we see now. Yes, evil occurs in our world now; but we must simply trust God that when we are finally able to understand his purposes we will be able to see that the suffering of people in the past and in the present is far outweighed by the good that is to come at some point in the future. Indeed, maybe the suffering of people in the past and in the present is actually *necessary* to bring about that future good. This is the idea that the world we experience is a 'Vale of tears', through which we must pass in order finally to attain to something which will make it all worthwhile. Possibly a few centuries ago this argument might have held some appeal; but there are surely few who have experienced, even at second hand through films and books, the horrors of the wars and the extermination camps of this century who can feel that this argument remains particularly persuasive. It would be inhuman to claim that it did.

Indeed, there have been plenty of people before our present century who have found this sort of optimistic argument highly unsatisfactory. (I call it 'optimistic' because it assumes that there will ultimately be a definite positive outcome to all the suffering of the world.) Perhaps because this topic touches so painfully upon us when we discuss it in terms of specific 'real life' instances, rather than in terms of philosophical generalities, some of the most vital discussions of it have actually been carried out in the pages of works of literature. In such works, specific instances may be discussed with all the fervour a writer can muster, without their necessarily being 'real'. Voltaire, for example, pilloried this sort of optimistic world-view mercilessly in his novel *Candide*, particularly in the person of Dr Pangloss: a man who, despite all the evidence to the contrary, persists in maintaining that all will be for the best in this, the best of all possible worlds. As an example of this character's topsy-turvy reasoning, consider his remark that 'Private misfortunes contribute to the general good, so that the more misfortunes there are, the more we find that all is well.'[17]

More seriously, the tortured intellectual Ivan Karamazov in Dostoevsky's mighty novel *The Brothers Karamazov* sets out the impossibility of this response to the problem of evil in perhaps the most remorselessly compelling way it has ever been expressed, by examining the cases of the torture and murder of innocent children. He concludes,

> If the sufferings of children go to make up the sum of sufferings which is necessary for the purchase of truth, then I say beforehand that the entire truth is not worth such a price ... I'd rather remain with my suffering unavenged and my indignation unappeased, even if I were wrong. Besides, too high a price has been placed on harmony. We cannot afford to pay so much for admission. And therefore I hasten to return my ticket of admission.[18]

Such arguments as this, which oppose the optimistic understanding of evil as something which is necessary in order to produce some greater good, seem to me unanswerable. Let us therefore move on, having noted them in all their force, to the other possible defences that might be made to the problem of evil.

Historically, probably the best-known response to the problem of evil is that of St Augustine. It is known as the free-will response. St Augustine held that God is indeed all-good, all-knowing and all-powerful; but that in addition, he has given to human beings the faculty of free will. We may use this faculty to choose either to follow God, and thereby to contribute to the good of the world, or to turn away from God, following our own evil ways. It is when we choose this latter course that evil arrives in the world. God is not responsible for it: we are, by choosing to turn against God.

There is a good deal to be said for this argument, in so far as it goes. Clearly human beings are indeed responsible by their actions for much of the evil in the world. The persecution of one individual or group by another, whether personal and petty or large-scale and systematic, is an obvious example. The evils of war are almost invariably brought about by mankind's rapacity and greed: the evils of famine, it might be argued, are brought about by mankind's selfishness in not sharing equitably the resources of our planet. But as has often been pointed out, what about those evils for which people really cannot be held responsible? What about, for example, earthquakes, hurricanes and the like: all those natural phenomena that are actually referred to by insurance companies as 'Acts of God'? (It was the terrible earthquake in Lisbon in 1755, which devastated the city and killed some 50,000 people, which was one of the events that prompted Voltaire to write *Candide*.)

Here, perhaps, the observations just made about the 'fine tuning' of the universe we inhabit can provide us with some insight. If God created the world we inhabit, then clearly he created it in a state of potential, in a state of becoming. He created it as a world in which life as we know it could, with the passing of time, come into existence. And, it would appear, he could not have made it very different to how it is if it were to be the kind of world that it is, a world in which we could come into being. God cannot, it is generally agreed, do what is logically impossible (create a four-sided triangle, for example): perhaps it was equally impossible for God to create a world in which we could come into being and which did not also contain the possibility of natural disasters occurring within it.

It might perhaps be asked, Why couldn't God intervene in the world to change natural laws and so prevent disasters? We thought briefly about this sort of interventionist God in an earlier chapter. Well, perhaps God could do just that. Perhaps he could arbitrarily flout physical laws. Two plus two can sometimes equal five: Winston Smith discovered that, in George Orwell's novel *1984*. But God could surely never be likened to the tyrannical Big Brother; and neither, for all the undeniable evil that exists within it, can our world properly be likened to room 101. I believe that for human beings to function as human beings we *need* the assurance of the regularity of natural laws. If we lacked that regularity in the world around us, we would simply drift helplessly within an ocean of unpredictability, unable to do anything, for learning would be impossible. God surely wishes us to grow as humans: for that to happen, a certain regularity in the processes of nature is essential.

What of the third of the counter-arguments to the problem of evil which I mentioned? Well, it follows on by extrapolation from this one. We have suggested that there are some things which God cannot do – things that are logically impossible, or logically prohibited by the construction of the universe. It follows from St Augustine's arguments, too, that God cannot simply force us into always choosing to do what he wants us to do: that would be to deny us true free will. In giving us free will, therefore, God must have voluntarily limited his power. What, then, if God is in fact *not* all-powerful, as we originally postulated he was when we defined the problem of evil?

The idea of God's omnipotence is in fact an attribute of God which was developed by writers in the early Church who, when seeking to describe God, chose naturally to do so in terms of the best prevailing philosophical–theological system of their day – that of neo-Platonism. The neo-Platonic God was very much that being to which absolutes could be applied – all-seeing, all-knowing, all-powerful and so on. The God of which we read in the Bible certainly has powerful attributes; but above all, the biblical God is the God of love. Christians believe, moreover, that God revealed himself, in the person of Jesus, in weakness rather than in power: would an all-powerful God have been crucified? And can the assertion 'God is love' (1 John 4. 8) actually be squared with the assertion 'God is all-powerful'? Surely it is of the very essence of love that it involves weakness: it involves setting aside one's own power over something or someone, be that power actual or potential, and allowing that thing or person its total autonomy. And that includes offering the loved one the option of rejecting the lover, as St Augustine recognized. Perhaps the best response that we can give to Ivan Karamazov is to say that God is all-good: he hates evil and suffering. God is also all-knowing: he is aware of the suffering of the world. But he is not all-powerful: he is unable to prevent that suffering. And perhaps a corollary of this should be that we reject another of those neo-Platonic ideas about God: that God is himself incapable of suffering. How can the lover possibly not be hurt by the pain of the beloved? Perhaps, when we begin to see God in this light, it becomes rather easier to respond positively to him in the aftermath of the horrors of our world in this century.

NOTES

1. For further reading on natural theology and revealed theology, see the articles 'Natural Theology' by Alan Richardson and John Macquarrie and 'Revelation' by David A. Pailin, in *A New Dictionary of Christian Theology*, eds Alan Richardson and John Bowden (SCM, 1983).

2. St Thomas Aquinas' vision, and its consequences, are widely reported. See, for example, T. Gilbey's biographical introduction to his selection and translation, *Philosophical Texts* by St Thomas (OUP, 1951), pp. xvi–xvii.

3. In Plato's writings we find many examples of God referred to in terms of abstract absolutes. For example, God is referred to as 'Ruler of all that is and shall be' (*Epistle VI*, 323 D). God is described as 'Utterly and perfectly righteous' (*Theaetetus*, 176 C): moreover, 'God desired that ... all things should be good and nothing evil' (*Timaeus*, 30 A). In addition, God created time whilst being himself eternal (*Timaeus*, 38 B ff.). Plotinus speaks of God in terms of 'The One' and 'The Intellectual–Principle'. These abstractions are, it seems to me, a long way from the passionate and loving God of whom we read in the Bible. (On Plato and Plotinus, see also Chapter 3, note 17.)

4. This quotation is from Robin Lane Fox's magisterial work *Pagans and Christians* (Penguin, 1988).

5. This story is taken from *The Sayings of the Desert Fathers*, trans. Benedicta Ward (Mowbray, revised edition 1984), p. 4. Further accounts of the deeds and aphorisms of the Desert Fathers can be found in *The Wisdom of the Desert*, trans. Thomas Merton (Darley

Anderson, 1988) and *The Lives of the Desert Fathers*, trans. Norman Russell (Mowbray, 1981).

6. See *Praying with St Francis*, trans. R. J. Armstrong and I. C. Brady (Triangle, 1987), pp. 3–4.

7. A highly readable translation of St John of the Cross's poetry is that of Roy Campbell (Collins, 1979).

8. St Augustine, *Confessions*, trans. Henry Chadwick (Oxford University Press, 1992), p. 295.

9. In an exquisite passage, Meister Eckhart writes: 'God is infinite in his simplicity and simple in his infinity. Therefore he is everywhere and is everywhere complete. He is everywhere on account of his infinity, and is everywhere complete on account of his simplicity . . . God is in the innermost part of each and every thing, only in its innermost part, and he alone is *one*.' See Latin Sermon 2 in *Meister Eckhart: Selected Writings*, trans. O. Davies (Penguin, 1994), p. 258. See also Davies' introduction to this selection, especially pp. xx ff.

10. Article by David A. Pailin on 'Process Theology', in *A New Dictionary of Christian Theology*, p. 467.

11. Such a world-view, based solely on the Bible, has never been achieved in the past, either. We have seen that early Church writers used 'pagan' philosophers extensively in constructing their world-view. Even the world-view of so explicitly Christian a period as the Middle Ages in Western Europe did the same: see C. S. Lewis' delightfully engaging study *The Discarded Image* (Canto, 1994), especially chapters III and IV.

12. R. Stannard, *Grounds for Reasonable Belief* (Scottish Academic Press, 1989), p. 326.

13. A broad survey of the anthropic principle in all its varied forms may be found in *The Anthropic Cosmological Principle* by J. D. Barrow and F. J. Tipler (Oxford University Press, 1986).

14. J. Leslie, *Universes* (Routledge, 1989), p. 64. This fascinating and very well-written book is warmly recommended, not least for the many marvellous stories which its author tells in order to expound his theses.

15. Ibid., p. 2.

16. One of the best studies of this whole area of theodicy – seeking to vindicate God's justice in a world in which evil exists – is that of John Hick, *Evil and the God of Love* (Macmillan, 1985).

17. Voltaire, *Candide*, trans. John Butt (Penguin, 1947), p. 31. This entertaining, if ultimately rather naïve, tale has been appropriately set to entertaining, if ultimately rather naïve, music by Leonard Bernstein.

18. F. M. Dostoevsky, *The Brothers Karamazov*, trans. David Magarshack (Penguin, 1982), p. 287. For my own interpretation of *The Brothers Karamazov* as a work of Christian apologetic, see *Theology*, xcviii (in press).

5

History and
myth

*No student of science has yet been taught that specific
gravity consists in the belief that Archimedes jumped out
of his bath and ran naked through the streets of Syracuse
shouting Eureka, Eureka, or that the law of inverse squares
must be discarded if anyone can prove that Newton was
never in an orchard in his life.*
        George Bernard Shaw, *Back to Methuselah*

I want to consider in this chapter some more of those 'What do we mean
by . . .?' questions. What do we mean by an historical fact? And what do
we mean by a myth? I then want to address the issue of the extent to which
the disciplines of science and theology use, or are dependent on, each of
them.

A word about history

History is, of course, the study of events that have taken place in the past,
through the examination of whatever items we may possess from the period
under study, in order to try to reconstruct and to understand those events
as fully as possible. These items may include written documents, or they
may perhaps be artistic artefacts, or remains unearthed by archaeologists.
It is often said that history has usually been written by the victors in any
struggle, be that struggle political, religious, military, or philosophical. We
might therefore expect our historical sources to reflect the outlooks of those
victors and not to give a very 'fair' picture of the outlook of the defeated
party. This is of course true, and so historians have to work hard to achieve

a balanced perspective when analysing past events. For example, they will examine documents produced by both sides when a conflict of some sort has taken place, whenever this is possible. (Of course, frequently it isn't, as the winners of such conflicts have a habit of destroying documents and other artefacts putting forward the points of view of the losers.)

When simple facts are concerned, it might be urged that history is capable of establishing information with a fair degree of certainty. That degree of certainty will tend to increase the closer in time the period under investigation is to our own. That such-and-such an event took place in such-and-such a location on such-and-such a date may be established in many cases without too much difficulty, particularly if we are thinking in terms of events in European history that have taken place in the last couple of centuries. For example, the tracing of family histories is becoming an increasingly popular activity. When carrying out such an exercise as this, the historian tries to ascertain years in which people were born, married and died, and this information may frequently be discovered through the examination of official registers, censuses, and the like. Let's take as a more specific example of an historical investigation such an attempt to trace a family's history, through the handing on of some property or other – a country estate, perhaps. There might well be very little difficulty in establishing such a succession of the property's owners, through looking at official records and registers held in local town halls and churches, assuming that no disaster has befallen them causing their destruction or loss. But problems arise if we wish our studies to proceed for any great distance on either of two fronts.

The first of these fronts is quite simply that of increasing time travelled into the past. The further back we go, the greater is the likelihood that registers will have been lost, damaged or destroyed, until finally we get to a point where they simply may not have been kept at all in any recognizable form. Our family history may just peter out, or there may at least be periods where it is impossible to determine any clear account of the succession. The second of these fronts is that of interpretation. Suppose we want to establish not just *what* happened, and *when*, but also *why*. There might perhaps be a point in the eighteenth century when the property appears to have passed not to the eldest son of the family, but to his younger brother. We might readily be able to establish the date *when* this happened, but to find out *why* it happened might be rather trickier. The records of local courts might reveal that the eldest son was tried for some crime (embezzlement, perhaps), was convicted, and was disinherited as a result: the eldest son's diary might miraculously have survived, in which he tells of his having been framed by his younger brother: another account written by a contemporary who knew the family might mention that one brother or the other is an inveterate liar; or maybe there is evidence to suggest that the court which convicted the elder brother was corrupt. Who, then, is to be believed? How are we to arrive at a plausible explanation of why the eldest son lost his inheritance?

Perhaps we may have evidence in favour of one interpretation that might make us choose it. The rest of the elder brother's diary, even reading between its lines, might show him to be an exceptionally pious and unsuspicious character – or, alternatively, might show him to be rather a shifty individual. Either of these readings might make us favour a particular explanation for his disinheritance. Evidence that the courts later overturned his conviction might emerge from further analysis of legal records, again favouring one particular account. However, unless some exceptional piece of evidence comes to light, the likelihood is that we will never know the true reason for this incident. Those seeking evidence for more wide-ranging arguments about judicial corruption or the misbehaviour of landed gentry might light on this as an example that illustrates the particular point they wish to make; but what such commentators are offering is, of course, an interpretation of what happened, not an account of 'historical fact'.

This example shows that whilst the bare bones of an historical event may be known – for example, the precise date on which a person was born/died/was disinherited – further information regarding *why* such an event happened may often be rather more equivocal. When we are using old texts (registers, diaries, biographies or whatever) to reconstruct history, we are necessarily interpreting them; and that process may very well involve the unintentional distortion of what 'really' happened, or possibly even its deliberate misrepresentation. A further complication comes in when we attempt to interpret philosophical, scientific or theological history. In such endeavours, it is of great importance that we also bear in mind a point which has been made by John Hedley Brooke, that 'Innovations be judged against the background of the prevailing knowledge at the time they were announced.'[1] It is all too easy to judge innovators or their ideas by present-day standards, and by the established success or otherwise that they have come to enjoy; but this is to be, in Brooke's words, 'profoundly unhistorical'. Such individuals must be set in their historical contexts if they are to be judged properly, on their own merits.

Science, theology and history

This discussion might seem to illustrate for us something that divides the scientist and the theologian. Both are in a sense involved in a dialogue with the events of the past, in that neither could proceed with their studies in the way in which they do without their disciplines having been developed in the way that, historically, they have been. However, it might be urged that, for the scientist, the events of the past – whilst they might be treated with a measure of respect – are largely irrelevant. The past is being continuously re-evaluated in the light of the present. A modern-day experiment is usually being carried out with more precise instrumentation and with a more complete understanding than any investigation in the past, so it makes sense to assume that it will give more accurate, and hence 'better', results. Historical events in the sciences are only important insofar as they have led to the present state of scientific understanding, and to the theories that obtain in the present. As George Bernard Shaw points out in the quotation at the head of this chapter, historical incidents, such as those which are popularly attributed to the lives of Archimedes and Newton, are utterly irrelevant to the particular insights which are alleged to have originated with them. Even the actual misrepresentation of past history would appear to be irrelevant to the present practice of a science. (This is true, at least, of the physical and biological sciences. As we have already seen, there are some scientific subjects, such as archaeology and palaeontology, in which history plays rather more significant a role. In fact, the principal aim of these sciences is to analyse finds from the past in order to derive from them accurate information about past events. Indeed, it is sometimes urged that the study of history can itself be regarded as a science. We shall not be concerned with these sorts of sciences in this chapter, however.)

In sharp contrast to this (it might be argued), theologians are necessarily concerned with the past of their discipline to a rather greater extent. They examine past reflections on the nature of God, as preserved in the books of the Bible and in the writings of earlier Christian authors, principally those whose works have been judged, with the hindsight of time, to be orthodox. And not only do theologians analyse the past. These orthodox works (it might be alleged) must remain the norm; and it follows from this that if new findings are to be admissible, then they must re-affirm old opinions. Present findings must always be in agreement with those of the past if they are to remain within the sphere of the orthodox. Past history is not just the passive subject matter of present-day theology: it actually takes an active part in shaping it.

But are these characterizations of the attitudes of science and of theology to their historical backgrounds actually true?

Theology and history

The activities of the theologian are necessarily rooted in history – in the events and characters encountered in the Bible, and in the writings of important authors throughout the history of the Church. However, we have seen that historical accounts, particularly those of events which took place long ago, necessarily involve an element of interpretation, both when ascertaining *what* happened, and also most certainly in attempting to give an account of *why* it happened. In the same way that historical 'fact' is difficult to unearth, then, theological 'fact' is very often similarly bound up with the interpretation of historical events.

The recognition of the importance of history to theological studies has led to many attempts to uncover 'real history' – to find out what 'really happened' – particularly when considering the events of the Bible. This entails the adoption of a critical approach to historical sources, to try to evaluate all biases within them, and later (and hence unreliable) additions to them. Such an approach has been developed massively in the past couple of centuries by historians in general, and by theologians in particular. A great deal of work in this field has been directed towards the Gospels, the accounts we possess of the life and teachings of Jesus, so much of the account that follows concerns the analysis of the Gospels. There has probably been more time and effort devoted to the detailed study of these very concise texts than to any other books ever written, as scholars have sought to establish concrete and unassailable information about that extraordinarily influential figure, Jesus of Nazareth. The various schools of study that have approached this area over the last century or so have sometimes been referred to as 'Quests for the Historical Jesus', a somewhat romantic-sounding title, but one that is perhaps appropriate in reflecting the ardour of those pursuing such 'quests' – as well as their seriousness.

It is perhaps worth noting to begin with that this search for facts, for 'the truth' about Jesus, originated during the late eighteenth and early nineteenth centuries. This was a time when many believed that the sciences were promising to deliver precisely 'the truth' about the cosmos. It might well be maintained that such quests for unassailable truth about the historical Jesus are now as anachronistic as the quest for inviolable truth in the sciences themselves. Interestingly, one of the greatest of modern New Testament scholars, E. P. Sanders, has tacitly made this point. He has introduced categories of *probability* in writing of events in Jesus' life, so that some events he reckons 'certain or virtually certain', some 'highly probable', some 'probable', some 'possible', some 'conceivable' (i.e. unlikely) and some 'incredible' (i.e. highly unlikely).[2] Ironically, in effectively doing away with the quest for certainty in what we can know about Jesus' life and teaching, Sanders is perhaps being the most 'scientific' of all New Testament commentators!

Jesus and history

The aim of scholars searching for definite information about Jesus was to discover the facts that underpin the Gospel narratives. It was taken for granted that these narratives could not be entirely factual from a purely historical point of view. This is, of course, a very big assumption. Four principal observations underpinned it.

First, there are some places where the Gospels contradict each other in what they tell us about Jesus. Second, the Gospels were not written by Jesus himself, and so they therefore necessarily reflect the views of their authors as well as those of Jesus himself. Even if a Gospel writer (an *Evangelist*, as they are known) added nothing at all to the facts of Jesus' life, his interpretation of the meanings of those facts would still be present simply by virtue of his having selected some material about Jesus to include in his account, and having left other material out of it (presumably, in both cases, for personal or practical reasons).

Third, the Gospels we possess were written some years after the events described in them took place. This point has two aspects to it. In the first place, the accounts themselves may be inaccurate, since the oldest of all the Gospels was probably written some thirty to forty years after the events described in it took place. Errors might have crept into the accounts of these events which reached the Gospel writer: additions to, or omissions from, what actually happened might have been made. In the second place, since the oldest copies of the Gospels are of course manuscripts, copied by hand, it is possible that errors were incorporated into them through the copying process during the period when this was the only way of reproducing books.

Fourth, the Gospel writers were people who inhabited a physical and a mental world very different to our own, in which, for example, people accepted that miracles could and did happen: so their ideas of what might be considered to be a historical fact probably differ a good deal from our own.

Let us examine these points one by one, starting with the contradictions that exist in the Gospel narratives.

To take an example of this, it has often been pointed out that the chronological sequence of events in the Gospels varies from one of them to another. In particular, the Gospels of Matthew, Mark and Luke (the so-called 'synoptic' Gospels, this name meaning that they frequently share a common viewpoint) often differ markedly from John's Gospel. This is the case even when they write about so important an event as the crucifixion of Jesus. Matthew, Mark and Luke place this event on the day after the Jewish festival of the Passover, so that the last supper which Jesus shares with his disciples on the night before his death is in fact the Passover meal. On the other hand, John has Jesus crucified on the day of the Passover itself. There is, quite clearly, a glaring inconsistency here. Does it mean that the accounts of these writers are not to be taken seriously as accounts of what actually happened to Jesus, since they can't even agree amongst themselves?

I think the significance of inconsistencies such as this can be exaggerated. It would surely be rather extreme to suggest that just because two accounts of an event – even one as central to the Christian faith as the crucifixion – are somewhat at odds with one another we cannot take *anything* in the Gospels seriously, or that we cannot even be certain that the event itself ever happened! Even today, eye-witness accounts of the same event can vary greatly in terms of the circumstantial details which they relate. Rather, it is surely more sensible to ask why John (who appears to be in the minority) should have written his account in defiance of what appears to have been the 'correct' sequence of events, as understood through the testimony of the other Evangelists.

One might well expect the way in which a history is written to depend on the preoccupations of the writer concerned. John is often very concerned to bring out the significance of Jesus' life and work in his Gospel. This is shown, for example, in the fact that the word which he uses to describe Jesus' miracles is not the same as that used by the other Evangelists, but is rather a word which is best translated as 'sign'. Jesus' miracles, for John, are not simply extraordinary works running contrary to natural expectations: rather, they are signposts, pointing towards the truth of who John believed Jesus to be. John also points out the similarities between the death of Jesus and the sacrifices of animals which were a part of Jewish ritual at the time of Jesus. These sacrifices were intended to bring about the forgiveness of people's sins: to effect their reconciliation with God. Thus when Jesus first appears in John's Gospel, he is referred to with the words, 'Here is the Lamb of God, who takes away the sin of the world!' (John 1. 29). In placing Jesus' death on the day of the Passover meal, John actually has Jesus die at the time when the lambs, which formed the central part of the Passover meal, were being slaughtered. We may therefore surely assume that the point which this writer is trying to make is a poetic, theological point, and that it is a point which he believes is more important than simple historical accuracy.

This approach – assessing the concerns of the writers involved in passages which contradict each other – is surely the only sensible one to make to such passages. And it takes us on to the second criticism that is sometimes made of the Gospels: that they were written not by

Jesus himself, but by other writers, who may or may not have been 'true to life' in their representations of him.

It is true that the accounts we have of Jesus' life were not written by him but by others, and naturally enough these other writers brought their own ideas and preoccupations to bear in writing their Gospels. This is also, of course, true of *any* historical biographical writing. Attempts have been made to evaluate what the particular contributions of each author are likely to have been, so that the authors' biases may be borne in mind when reading the text. This evaluation may be made through a close comparison of the different Gospel texts, which can show ways in which the preoccupations of the individual Gospel writers influenced the way in which they shaped their material. This approach is sometimes called 'Redaction Criticism' (a redactor is an editor).

For example, it may readily be seen that Matthew frequently quotes Old Testament prophecies in his Gospel, most notably perhaps in his account of the events around Jesus' birth. The words 'This was to fulfil what had been spoken by the Lord through the prophet', or their equivalent, occur no fewer than five times in the first two chapters of Matthew's Gospel alone. It thus seems quite likely that Matthew was writing his Gospel for people from a Jewish background, who would understand these references and their significance. It also seems reasonable to infer that Matthew himself probably hailed from the same sort of background. We can never know these things for certain, of course; but it seems a pretty fair inference to say, at the very least, that the writer of this Gospel was steeped in Jewish culture, and shared expectations derived from that culture with those whom he intended to read his book.

It might be thought that this sort of analysis implies that Matthew (and, similarly, the other Evangelists) is presenting us not with an 'authentic' account of Jesus' life, but rather with a selective and personal version of it. Anybody writing about another person brings to them their own perceptions: that is only to be expected. It has been commented that all the writers who have ever attempted to write about the 'historical Jesus' have also wound up simply writing about how they themselves wished to perceive Jesus, recent writers no less than early ones. The analogy has been made with people looking down a deep well, and seeing their own reflection at the bottom. Doubtless I, too, write about such matters as these very much from my own perspective. However, whilst the accounts we have of Jesus may be written through the prism of another person's perceptions, it is surely likely that an authentic 'flavour' of the person being described is transmitted. For those who remain sceptical, further 'tests' have been devised by scholars to ascertain the likelihood of particular incidents described in the Gospels as being genuine.

One such test is 'multiple attestation': if an incident about Jesus is recounted by two or more independent sources for his life, the likelihood of its historical truth is increased. Another is the 'criterion of dissimilarity': sayings or events ascribed to Jesus are likely to be authentic if there are no parallels to them to be observed in the writings of the early Church or in the writings of Jesus' Jewish contemporaries. Material which is totally unique in this way is likely to have come from Jesus himself. Of course, criteria like these cut two ways. We have a very limited number of independent sources from which to derive information about Jesus, and those outside the Bible tell us next to nothing about him other than that he lived, that he was executed, and that he subsequently had many followers. With regard to the criterion of dissimilarity, why should the early Church have bothered to preserve incidents about Jesus that it wasn't likely to find useful or appropriate to its own situation, and therefore that its writers would be likely to allude to, or even to quote? Any incidents that were preserved by chance in this way are not likely to be very interesting ones. Given that Jesus' background was unequivocally Jewish, is it not highly probable that he would have reflected that cultural background in his words and deeds? Any incidents that do not reflect this are in all probability quite uncharacteristic, even if they are also genuine. It seems to me that very little of any interest may be determined about Jesus from this sort of highly sceptical approach. Moreover, the little we can glean gives us a picture of a rather eccentric individual, completely cut off from both past and future. Still, for those of a particularly sceptical turn of mind, such approaches at least yield very strong probabilities of historical authenticity, if not absolute certainty of historical fact.

What about our third point, that the Gospels were written long after the events they describe, and that they may have been corrupted in their transmission? Well, it seems likely that Jesus died in around the year 30 CE, and the earliest Gospel account that we have (probably that of St Mark, although this remains a hotly debated issue) is generally dated to around 65 CE. There is therefore a significant gap between the events of Jesus' life and our earliest record of them. Moreover, it is also the case that in all probability even the oldest manuscripts we possess are copies of copies, and changes and alterations are likely to have occurred during the copying process that came between them and the original Gospels. Such changes may be trivial omissions of a word here and there, or they may be more important. For example, the oldest copies of Mark's Gospel do not have verses 9–20 of Chapter 16, and hence these are widely believed to be later (though probably not very much later) additions. John's Gospel seems to finish neatly at the end of Chapter 20, with the writer commenting that Jesus did many things which are not written in his book, and explaining that he has written what he has in order that the reader 'May come to believe that Jesus is the Messiah, the Son of God', and 'May have life in his name' in consequence (John 20. 30–31). This neat conclusion would appear to suggest, from a literary point of view, that Chapter 21, with its 'second ending', was a later addition, like the final verses of Mark's Gospel (although in the case of John there is no evidence to support this hypothesis to be found in early manuscripts, since none exist which lack Chapter 21).

One other way in which the Gospels have been analysed is by the separation of the narratives they contain into small, apparently independent, chunks. This is the basis of what is known as 'Form Criticism'. It is suggested by the advocates of this method that the short stories of which the Gospels are largely composed were originally preserved independently of one another, handed on by word of mouth by Jesus' followers. They further suggest that this brought about a selection process, in preserving predominantly the short stories which were, for whatever reason, of importance to the earliest Christians. Form critics therefore seek to understand the original settings of stories of and about Jesus in the life of the early Church, in order to understand better the 'lens' of the early Church through which our pictures of Jesus are refracted. Incidentally, this approach to the Gospels puts very little emphasis on the Evangelists as anything other than the compilers of the Gospels. They are viewed as people who simply set down all these little stories about Jesus in order, a process sometimes likened to the threading of pearls on to a string. It was to correct this obviously over-simplified understanding of the part which the Gospel writers themselves played in producing the texts which we now possess that saw the advent of redaction criticism, as discussed above.[3]

Just to put all of these rather sceptical approaches to the Gospels into some sort of perspective, however, consider other writers of similar antiquity to the Evangelists, such as the Roman authors Tacitus and Caesar. Tacitus wrote his *Annals* probably in the early years of the second century CE: they describe events going back almost a century from the time of writing. Yet Tacitus is generally reckoned a reliable historian of the period. Again, Caesar's *Gallic Wars*, written in the first century BCE, is generally reckoned a more or less accurate historical source; however, the oldest manuscript we have of this book was written nearly one thousand years after the events described in it. The oldest manuscripts we possess of the entire New Testament (in Greek, of course) date from the fourth century, whilst what is currently reckoned to be the oldest fragment (the Rylands Papyrus, on which is written verses from John's Gospel) has been dated to the first half of the second century.

In other words, yes, there is a gap between the writing of our Gospels and the events which they describe; but it is by no means a big one compared to other ancient histories. Yes, there is a tremendous gulf in time between our world and that of the first century CE; but it is bridged by manuscripts of an antiquity and closeness to the events they describe which (for that period) can hardly be bettered. Let us at least be consistent in our judgements of the historical value of ancient sources like these.

What about our fourth point, that the world-view of Jesus and his contemporaries is very different to our own? A view often expressed is that people of Jesus' day were much more gullible than people today: they believed in miracles and the like, and hence they cannot be relied upon to have given us a very reliable picture of Jesus from an historical point of view. But is this picture really true? The New Testament writers record the scepticism which their words provoked in many of their contemporaries. St Paul reckoned that the message he proclaimed was 'folly' to those who considered themselves wise by the world's standards (see 1 Corinthians 1. 18 ff.), and the sceptical crowd who witnessed the extraordinary behaviour of the disciples on the day of Pentecost inferred from their behaviour that they were drunk (see Acts 2. 13)! The suggestion that all the people of this period were gullible simpletons, who were very uncritical towards allegedly miraculous happenings, does not stand up well to scrutiny. Moreover, our own alleged lack of gullibility is perhaps given the lie by the popularity of the semi-fictitious tabloid press in our own day!

However, there clearly are differences between Jesus' world and our own. One aspect of the Gospels which was largely accepted for a long time, but which has undoubtedly attracted a good deal of scepticism in the last couple of centuries, is the occurrence of miracle stories within them; so let's now consider the subject of miracles in a little more detail.

The miracles

The accounts of Jesus' miracles might be dismissed out of hand by the very sceptical as pure fabrications, but this does not seem to me to be the best approach to take, since they appear to form an integral part of all four Gospels. Three alternative views of the miracles are possible, which may be summarized as follows.

First, the miracles happened exactly as the Evangelists recorded them. They impressed people in Jesus' day, and they're there in the Gospels to impress people today, too. They might even be seen as proofs of Jesus' divinity, and vindications of the authority of his teachings. Jesus actually physically healed people of blindness, lameness, leprosy, and so on: he actually walked on water, and calmed storms; and he actually miraculously multiplied small quantities of bread and fish in order to feed crowds of 4000 and 5000 people.

Second, the miracles may or may not have a basis in fact, but are employed by the Evangelists, or by the sources which they used, primarily in order to illustrate vital truths about who Jesus was, about his power and his authority, and so on. Their importance lies not in their literal truth, but rather in the things which they illustrate or symbolize. The healing miracles illustrate the healing power of God, the nature miracles illustrate the authority of God over the natural world, the feeding miracles illustrate the way in which God feeds and nourishes his people, and so on.

The third view of the miracles is that they are stories about events which actually happened, but these events were not in fact miraculous: they were simply interpreted as such by the rather credulous people of Jesus' day. So, for example, the healings done by Jesus were effectively faith healings: the people concerned were healed psychologically, through their faith. Jesus didn't walk on water, but rather on a barely submerged sand bar, which only he knew about. The feeding miracles represent in fact large 'bring and share' suppers; inspired by Jesus' example of sharing the small amount of food he had with him, everybody else who was present brought out the food they had with them and shared it with those around them. Other allegedly miraculous happenings have also been explained in this way.

This third approach has led some of its proponents into quite phenomenally tortuous interpretations of Jesus' miracles in order to preserve their alleged basis in non-miraculous incidents which might have been interpreted as miraculous by those around him. It is not an approach I personally find particularly convincing. However, neither am I swayed by the completely literal interpretation of the miracle stories (the first of the approaches which I suggested above). So – what if their origin may not lie exclusively in historical fact, but may be at least in part an elaboration of facts by the Gospel writers? Such an elaboration of facts, I suggest, gives rise to what is commonly called a 'myth'. Let us now ask, what exactly do we mean by this word?

A word about myths

Many people who profess religious beliefs get rather upset at the use of a word like 'myth'. It is thought to imply a story that is, at bottom, not true. Let me therefore first make one thing clear: a myth, as I understand the word, is *not* simply something that is untrue. A myth may or may not be based on actual historical incidents; but its continuation, the handing-down of the myth from generation to generation, means that it has a purpose, a truth contained in it, which may or may not be connected to the actual events the myth describes. If I refer to some of the stories about Jesus as 'mythical', that does not mean I believe them to be untrue: it means that I believe that we must search for the truth contained in them at other than a literal level. We have seen an example of this approach already, in the way in which we approached St John's dating of Jesus' crucifixion. Perhaps, in general, a good place to begin such searching for the truths contained in stories like these is to ask why the stories have persisted in being told. Why should stories about Jesus (or, indeed, about anyone else) persist if it appears unlikely that they are literally true? Presumably because the story has some other thing to communicate apart from its literal truth. Put like this, I have no difficulty in understanding things I find otherwise incomprehensible about Jesus. The miracle stories are true, in that they show that Jesus, as God, transcended the natural order: they are also true in that they point towards the healing, the making whole, of nature, which is often asserted by theologians as being God's ultimate desire for it.[4] The truth of stories – of myths – such as these is a truth in the here and now, not in their historical accuracy: that is, by comparison, irrelevant.

In case this statement sounds rather strange, let me give another example of what I mean, this time from the world of literature. Consider the following passage from the Russian author Mikhail Bulgakov's great novel *The Master and Margarita*.

The house was called 'Griboyedov's House' because it might once have belonged to an aunt of the famous playwright Alexander Sergeyevich Griboyedov. Nobody really knows for sure whether she ever owned it or not. People even say that Griboyedov never had an aunt who owned any such property . . . Still, that was its name. What is more, a dubious tale used to circulate in Moscow of how in the round, colonnaded salon on the second floor the famous writer had once read extracts from 'Woe from Wit' to that same aunt as she reclined on a sofa. Perhaps he did; in any case, it doesn't matter.[5]

The house is called Griboyedov's House, and has very special associations as a result (in the novel, it is being used as the headquarters of a large Moscow literary club). There are alleged literary resonances to the place, immortalized in its name: the importance of that name, though, lies in the present, not in whether or not the stories of the past are true. In a sense, the continued importance of the name is proof enough of the validity of the old stories about the place, since otherwise they would no longer be circulating. The truth of the stories about the house lies in their having a real value in the present, in terms of the effect they have on people's lives *now*.

Myths may well originate in facts. Griboyedov's aunt may, indeed, once have lived in the house that now bears his name. However, Bulgakov leaves the question open: 'in any case, it doesn't matter'. Similarly, the myths we have recorded about Jesus in the Gospels may well originate in fact. However, I would urge that whether or not this is the case *doesn't matter*. The truth of the myths is borne out by their continued validity and importance in people's lives in the present. Jesus lived, and was remarkable in all that he showed us about God, in his life, in his teachings, and in his death. The miracle stories also show us important things about God. For people in the past, the miracles provided confirmation of the truth of Jesus' identity, but it should not worry us unduly if we today find such confirmation in other aspects of the Gospel records about him.

History and myth

We may go further than this. We have seen that interpretation is important in writing an account of history. Such interpretations will surely never be wholly accurate. They will reflect the biases of the sources used; and, even more fundamentally, they will reflect the views of the writer of the modern account. Is it therefore so far wide of the mark to suggest that there is actually a mythic element in the reconstruction of *any* past event? That element may be small in the case of recent, well-documented history, or it may be larger in the case of events in the remote past, or about which information is scarce. Consider an event like the Norman conquest of England. The evidence is quite unequivocal in pointing towards its actually having happened; but are there not aspects of that event which have taken on a mythical quality for anyone born in England? The bold invaders, few in number, subduing a rough, lawless and divided people and laying the foundations of a nation that was never again to be conquered by any foreign enemy: this can all too often be the sort of gloss that is a part of English people's understanding of the Norman conquest. But the actual events of that conquest were considerably messier, and the consequences of that conquest considerably more equivocal, than this very simplistic understanding implies.

In short, I would urge that in the same way that 'belief' and 'knowledge' are not the poles-apart concepts that they are sometimes held to be, but, rather, each contains an element of the other, so too with history and myth. Histories contain glosses and biases in their presentation reflecting the opinions of their authors and do not give utterly accurate pictures of the past, but rather more or less mythical ones: myths, which may consist in some cases very largely of elaboration, may still frequently have been based on historical incidents. I have no hesitation in referring to Noah's flood as a myth, for example, even though I am well aware that there is archaeological evidence from the Mediterranean basin to suggest that a great flood did indeed happen there in prehistoric times. That this myth may well be based on fact is irrelevant.

The process of myth-making can be seen going on around us every day. Imagine a news report of some incident involving hostile powers. One side may claim the incident was an act of aggression by its adversaries: they in turn may claim that it was an act of defence on their part. Who is correct? The way that the incident is reported on the news in Britain will tend to depend on which side has the sympathies of the British. (One would hope that this would be the side deserving these sympathies, but one has no means of guaranteeing this.) So, 'news' is in fact, at least in part, opinion: in the same way, 'history' is, at least in part, myth.

Science and history

We certainly seem to have witnessed a distinct parting of the ways between science and theology in this chapter. However, let us now turn to the relationship between history and the scientific enterprise, and, in doing so, draw on what we have observed in our discussion so far. There are two issues to be discussed here. First, to what extent can – and indeed should – science proceed independently of past history? Second, what about myths? Though irrelevant in theory to science, does it in fact use them in practice?

It is clearly not the case that science is *totally* divorced from its past history. The past findings of science, leading to the current understandings of what is 'true', obviously have an effect on the particular experiments which are done in the present. Although many experiments might theoretically be carried out by a person with only the vaguest understanding of the wider historical context of the scientific research of which that experiment is a part, science as an endeavour may only be advanced if past theories are understood, and if present data are interpreted in the light of them.

Moreover, it is surely only when past theories are fully understood that their overturning in the sort of 'scientific revolution' of which Kuhn wrote can come about. Scientific progress is not random or blind: rather, the past history of science shapes the overall strategies of science in the present. It may even exert an influence on the way in which observations are carried out in any particular experiment.

It was suggested earlier in this chapter that misrepresentation of the past in science would be largely irrelevant, since it would not in any way affect the way in which science was carried out in the present. An idea that has been judged of scientific value can stand independently of the way in which it was first generated. But scientists themselves cannot stand outside the course of history, and their actual words and deeds are events in history. In the same way as with biblical stories, those words and deeds may come to contain elements of mythical elaboration. Even though the scientific discoveries connected with those scientists are not invalidated by such elaboration it is interesting to observe that it happens. *Why* it should happen, though, is more complex. To think about this issue, let's now examine the particular case of a scientist around whose life a great deal of elaboration and comment has taken place.

Everyone has heard of Galileo, the Italian astronomer. His work developing the Copernican hypothesis (that the earth goes around the sun, not vice versa) famously led to his condemnation by the Church of his day, the generally accepted teaching of which maintained that the sun revolved around the earth. Following his trial by the Church authorities, Galileo recanted the views which he had expressed. He tends to be remembered as something of a scientific hero-figure, the lone voice which spoke out the truth in the face of hostile, bigoted opposition.[6] But is such an understanding of him – and of the Church and society of his day – historically correct? Might not this in fact be just one more example of history being written by the victors?

John Hedley Brooke has noted: 'It would ... be quite wrong to imagine that opposition to the Copernican theory derived only from religious prejudice. In 1543 an earth-centred cosmos was the physical orthodoxy of the day, supported by philosophical arguments that, at the time, were particularly compelling.'[7] It was not just the Church that disputed the accuracy of the Copernican theory: many scientists of the day did so too. Still, it was upon Galileo rather than Copernicus that condemnation fell. Why should this have been so? C. S. Lewis, in a study of the medieval and Renaissance thought-world, writes:

The real reason why Copernicus raised no ripple and Galileo raised a storm, may well be that whereas the one offered a new supposal about celestial motions, the other insisted on treating this supposal as fact. If so, the real revolution consisted not in a new theory of the heavens but in 'a new theory of the nature of theory'.[8]

Lewis maintains that Copernicus had pointed out that the movements of the sun, moon and planets were such that it was 'as if' the earth revolved around the sun. His contemporaries had few difficulties with this: it was an interesting idea, even if it didn't intuitively make as much sense as the older viewpoint. But Galileo insisted that what might *appear to be* the case actually *was* so. In the terms which we used in Chapter 2, Copernicus' views were treated in a non-realist way, in line with the general approach of his age: Galileo, on the other hand, was a realist, and a rather extreme one, too. It was this philosophical position on Galileo's part, rather than his scientific ideas, that led to the Church's opposition to him.

Paul Feyerabend agrees with this analysis, and goes even further. He maintains that:

The experts declared the [Copernican] doctrine . . . to be unscientific. This judgment was made without reference to faith, or to church doctrine, but was based exclusively on the scientific situation of the time. It was shared by many scientists . . . *and it was correct* when based on the facts, the theories and the standards of the time.[9]

Feyerabend accuses Galileo of sloppy and ill-conceived reasoning, and of using propaganda rather than logical methods to popularize his ideas. He summarizes his argument thus:

The Church at the time of Galileo not only kept closer to reason as defined then and, in part, even now; it also considered the ethical and social consequences of Galileo's views. Its indictment of Galileo was rational and only opportunism and a lack of perspective can demand a revision.[10]

So why does Galileo have his present-day reputation? Feyerabend believes that 'It is not a concern for humanity but rather party interests which play a major role in the Galileo hagiography.'[11] In short, Galileo may only be seen as the one who 'got it right' with the considerable benefit of hindsight. By the standards that applied in his day, it was the authorities who were in the right, and they actually treated him rather leniently. We only perceive him as the correct party in the argument with the authorities of his day because we, now, side with him in our understanding of the cosmos. This is surely a classic case of the winning side of an argument being unfair to the losers of it.

Other interpretations of Galileo's character and motives have been suggested, some of them still more at odds with the view of Galileo as a hero-figure. For example, Bertolt Brecht's play *The Life of Galileo* portrays Galileo as a craven, cowardly individual, who, in recanting his astronomical ideas, failed to achieve all that he might have done in the cause of scientific progress. Towards the end of the play, Galileo remarks:

> As a scientist I had a unique opportunity. In my day, astronomy emerged into the market place. Given this unique situation, if one man had put up a fight it might have had tremendous repercussions. Had I stood firm the scientists could have developed something like the doctors' Hippocratic oath, a vow to use their knowledge exclusively for mankind's benefit . . . I was never in any real danger. For a few years I was as strong as the authorities. And I handed my knowledge to those in power for them to use, fail to use, misuse – whatever best suited their objectives.[12]

In the end, though, Galileo's ideas are preserved. His final treatise is smuggled abroad for publication, but its author is described as having 'Stained hands'. Galileo comments, 'Better stained than empty.'[13] Science progresses inexorably: heroism, or the lack of it, is an irrelevance.

Hero, coward or irrational and potentially dangerous opportunist? The 'real' Galileo was, no doubt, in one sense none of these things, and in another sense all of them, and more. His portrayal by a writer will naturally depend on the viewpoint of the writer concerned, who will emphasize certain aspects of his life whilst suppressing others in order to make a desired point. Brecht writes as a polemical dramatist, and Feyerabend as a philosophical controversialist; but whatever a writer's motivation may be, a biographical account of another person's life will almost inevitably contain an element of 'myth' alongside 'fact'. This happens, at least in part, in order to serve the purposes of the writer concerned.

This sort of debate over the philosophical and moral character of a person now long dead and unable to defend himself may strike you as rather unfair. (I choose Galileo simply because of the considerable interest that he has aroused in later writers.) In any case, it might be said, how can this sort of issue actually have any impact on the way in which science is conducted in the here and now? In a sense, it doesn't. Galileo's findings stand independently of the man, and of his character (whatever that may have been like). But does this mean that scientists may feel free to claim some kind of moral *carte blanche* so far as their investigations are concerned – that future vindication validates present iniquity? Can it be assumed that the scientific end will always justify the means? Is there such a thing as 'immoral' science? Can scientists 'go too far' in the pursuit of their discipline – and who defines what that 'too far' is? To use Brecht's image, is it more important for a scientist that his or her hands be full of practical achievements than that they be unstained? The vital importance of questions like these in our day, particularly in fields such as genetic engineering and other forms of medical research, is something that we cannot afford to overlook, even if there are no easy answers to them.

The picture of Galileo as Champion of the Truth, then, is something of a myth. Thinking more generally, what sort of relevance can myths have to science? Myths may surround the life of a scientist in the past, but surely there is no place for them in the actual practice of science in the present? One might well think not. It is of course true that the sciences use models as aids, and these are acknowledged not to be literal representations of the truth; but these are not myths as we have been discussing them. Models do not point to truths beyond the information they themselves contain, whilst myths do. However, the myths of science exist, and can have a practical effect, in terms of the inspiration and sense of security which they provide for practising scientists. The different scientific disciplines have their various hero-figures (such as Galileo), who may be looked upon with reverence – as examples of inspired thinking, perhaps, or of good practice. I'd like now to discuss a more recent example of a scientific myth, which may be seen in the story of the debate which took place in Oxford in 1860 between T. H. Huxley and Bishop Wilberforce, at that time the Bishop of Oxford, over the theories of Darwin.

The palaeontologist Stephen Jay Gould rates this debate alongside the stories of Newton and Archimedes as 'Among the half-dozen greatest legends of science'.[14] It is a confrontation that has gone down in history as an occasion when the scientific viewpoint put the theological one to rout. Gould quotes a modern version he considers to be 'average', that of Ruth Moore:

For half an hour the Bishop spoke savagely ridiculing Darwin and Huxley, who sat with him on the platform. In tones icy with sarcasm, he put his famous question: was it through his grandfather or grandmother that he claimed descent from an ape? . . . [Huxley] tore into the arguments Wilberforce had used . . . Working himself up to his climax, he shouted that he would feel no shame in having an ape as an ancestor, but that he would be ashamed of a brilliant man who plunged into scientific questions of which he knew nothing . . . The issue had been joined. From that hour on, the quarrel over the elemental issue that the world believed was involved, science versus religion, was to rage unabated.[15]

However, as Gould goes on to say, the available evidence does not support this account of the affair. And as the philosopher Mary Midgley has written,

Contemporary accounts do not bear out the version of it [the debate] we were brought up on. Wilberforce (it emerges) certainly did not just waffle and appeal to irrelevant feeling. He made clear, forceful and pertinent scientific criticisms, which were seen as such by Darwin himself . . . Wilberforce was, after all, not present as a bishop, but as a scientist, vice-president of the British Academy, with good ornithological work to his credit, and spokesman for Sir Richard Owen, the greatest anatomist of the day . . . Just what he did finally say to upset Huxley we shall probably never know. Neither his remark nor Huxley's reply was sufficiently noticed to be reported.[16]

Midgley suggests that the later version of this encounter simply 'Grew naturally out of the hindsight of the victors'.

J. R. Lucas is even more damning of the mythical version of this debate. He examines all extant contemporary accounts of it, from those written subsequently by the protagonists to those of journalists who were present, and comments:

All in all, Wilberforce's speech was well suited to the occasion. Although it did not find favour with the Darwinians, it not only succeeded in communicating to a large and fractious audience new and difficult ideas, but put forward serious arguments and made a number of telling points, which . . . Huxley did not succeed in meeting effectively.[17]

Why, then, does such a myth persist, if it is demonstrably a laundering, if not a total fabrication, of the events that actually took place? Lucas puts it down at least in part to the pugnacious and rather insecure personality of Huxley himself:

The Darwinians, who were a small minority in 1860, became the dominant majority over the next twenty years, but never lost the sense of being persecuted. This was partly a matter of Huxley's own personality. He had no love of ecclesiastics and was sure that science must be at odds with religion. Later in his life he is still remarkably resistant to the idea that there were clergymen who accepted evolution, even when actually faced with them ... The quarrel between religion and science came about not because of what Wilberforce said, but because it was what Huxley wanted; and as Darwin's theory gained supporters, they took over his view of the incident.[18]

Gould, too, attributes the mythical account of this event to Huxley's anticlericalism, and to his need to set up a 'cardboard dichotomy' between science and organized religion. Lucas and Midgley both comment on Huxley's desire to establish professional specialisms in science, moving the sciences away from being the preserve of the gentleman 'naturalist' – Wilberforce himself being an example of this kind of 'part-time' approach to science. Not only the hated clerics, but also the despised scientific amateurs, might therefore be considered to have been routed in the mythical account of this debate.

Of course, as we have seen, once a myth like this becomes established, its effects are long-lasting, and its literal truth irrelevant. But why should it become established in the first place? Perhaps, like some more obviously 'religious' myths, it has persisted because it fulfils a psychological need: because it justifies present attitudes by purporting to establish them so firmly that there is no necessity for continued debate. Maybe Darwinists ever since 1860 have perceived an antagonism to their doctrines originating from religious sources (sadly, as pointed out in Chapter 1, that perception is sometimes an accurate one). Could it therefore be that they are anxious to have a 'foundation myth' of their own – Huxley prevailing over Wilberforce, as the Children of Israel prevailed over their foes in the biblical myths? Perhaps a subconscious validation of what one is doing arises from such a myth: that, indeed, may be a part of the purpose of the myth in the first place. Darwinists are, after all, only human, and we all need to feel that our theories (whatever they may be) are validated in some way. I hope, in any case, that this example serves to illustrate the universality of myths, and their importance and relevance within the sciences as well as within religious systems.

In conclusion, we have observed in this chapter (as in the other chapters of this book) that there are indeed differences between science and theology, in this case in the attitudes of these disciplines to history and to myth. However, once again we may observe that the differences are differences of scale, not of kind. History and myth are both important in theology, and may sometimes be so closely bound together as to be inseparable. History is relevant to the development of science, though its precise interpretation is probably not as important in the sciences as it is in theology. Moreover, myths are significant within the scientific community as well as within the theological one. Both scientific and theological activities may be founded upon them, and they have a part to play in facilitating the progress of both these fields of human enquiry.

In fact, the alleged gulf between science and theology may be seen as a myth itself: a myth perpetuated by those of scientific or religious persuasions who wish to defend their own position against the perceived assaults of others. This particular myth, though, is an extremely unhelpful one. I believe that the way ahead for all intellectual disciplines lies in co-operation, collaboration and mutual instruction, not in the shouting of outdated and misconceived accusations from behind entrenched positions. Science and theology need each other. They are both a part of the great and unending quest of humankind to discover more about itself, and about its place in, and relationship with, the cosmos. As in any other great and worthwhile quest, allies are of far greater value than opponents.

NOTES

1. J. H. Brooke, *Science and Religion: Some Historical Perspectives* (Cambridge University Press, 1991), p. 36.
2. See E. P. Sanders, *Jesus and Judaism* (SCM Press, 1985), p. 326.
3. For a historical perspective on the development of biblical criticism, see Stephen Neill's and Tom Wright's *The Interpretation of the New Testament 1861–1986* (Oxford University Press, 2nd edition, 1988). For detailed accounts of the methods and findings of the critical approaches described here, and others besides, see E. P. Sanders' and Margaret Davies' *Studying the Synoptic Gospels* (SCM Press, 1989), especially parts three and four. For a brief introduction to the quests for the historical Jesus, and a sensible riposte to some of the more outlandish versions of Jesus' life and work that have appeared recently, see Tom Wright's *Who Was Jesus?* (SPCK, 1992).
4. Probably the best-known theological writer to have spoken in terms of a future wholeness of the universe is Pierre Teilhard de Chardin. In his book *The Phenomenon of Man* (English trans. Collins, 1959) he develops the idea of the 'Omega point' towards which the cosmos is evolving, and in which all of creation is destined to find fulfilment.
5. M. Bulgakov, *The Master and Margarita*, trans. Michael Glenny (Everyman's Library, 1992), p. 57.
6. Although it is not quite so extreme, C. A. Ronan's *Cambridge Illustrated History of the World's Science* (Cambridge University Press, 1983) may be cited as giving an example of the 'traditional' view of Galileo (see pp. 339–43). He is presented very much as the man

who 'got it right', and no attempt whatsoever is made to understand why his contemporaries might have thought otherwise.

7. J. H. Brooke, op. cit. p. 37.
8. C. S. Lewis, *The Discarded Image* (Canto, 1994), p. 16. (Lewis is himself quoting A. O. Barfield's *Saving the Appearances*.)
9. P. Feyerabend, *Against Method* (Verso, revised edition, 1988), p. 132.
10. Ibid., p. 129.
11. Ibid., p. 131.
12. B. Brecht, *The Life of Galileo*, trans. John Willett (in Brecht, *Plays: Three*, Methuen, 1987), p. 109.
13. Ibid., p. 106.
14. S. J. Gould, *Bully for Brontosaurus* (Penguin, 1992), p. 386.
15. Ibid., pp. 386–7. To be fair, at least one modern biography of Darwin points out the many ambiguities present in the accounts we have of the 1860 debate, although it effectively continues the Darwinists' policy of vilifying Wilberforce (see A. Desmond and J. Moore, *Darwin* (Michael Joseph Ltd., 1991), pp. 492–9). Perhaps more accurate presentations of this debate will never be popular, because they are so much less exciting than the mythical version.
16. M. Midgley, *Evolution as a Religion* (Methuen, 1985), p. 11.
17. J. R. Lucas, 'Wilberforce and Huxley: A Legendary Encounter', *The Historical Journal*, vol. 22 (1979), p. 323.
18. Ibid., p. 329.

6

Language

Oh quanto è corto il dire e come fioco
al mio concetto! e questo, a quel ch'io vidi,
è tanto che non basta a dicer poco.
Dante, Paradiso, canto 33, 120–2

When addressing the subject of the languages used in the worlds of science and theology, we certainly appear to have a necessary divide between them. This would appear to be the case at two levels: first, they use different vocabularies appropriate to their different subjects; and second, they use words in different ways. That the vocabularies of the two disciplines are different is clear: theologians use words that are felt to be appropriate to talk about God, and scientists use words that are felt to be appropriate to talk about the physical world. The two disciplines are set up in order to investigate different things, and use vocabularies appropriate to their investigations. However, even if science and theology do use different vocabularies, this surely need not be a source of *antagonism* between them, any more than the different vocabularies used by chefs and car mechanics need be.

When we come to the way in which language is used by each of the disciplines, though, the differences between them might appear more acute and important. It simply does not appear possible to talk about God in the same way that we talk about the things we observe in the physical world. There, we apply our words directly to the things we observe: we speak of laws which bodies in motion may be observed to obey, we speak of the component parts of a substance as revealed by its microscopic, chemical or spectroscopic analysis, and so on. Whether one adopts a realist or a non-realist understanding of scientific theories, it would in either case appear that our language maps pretty well directly on to the things we are talking about. On the other hand, the way in which we use language about God can appear ambiguous, and indeed, from a literal point of view, even false. Remember those words addressed to God by the Psalmist, 'You make the clouds your chariot, and ride upon the wings of the wind' (Psalm 104). This statement is obviously not 'true' in the sense that the statement 'The wind is blowing at a speed of 25 kilometres per hour' could be true. We are here talking about the ambiguity of figurative statements as opposed to the clarity of literal ones.

Let us now see how accurate these characterizations of the ways in which language is used by science and by theology turn out to be on closer inspection.

The language of science

Let's begin by asking whether the language of science is always quite as precise as I've suggested. By and large, no doubt, scientists do use language in very clear and unambiguous ways, but I would maintain that they do not always do so, and that there are actually sometimes occasions when scientific ideas may helpfully be expressed in less clear ways.

For example, consider the humble electron. This entity always used to be – and indeed frequently still is – described as a particle, and there is plenty of available evidence to justify that description. The observation that an atom may be given an electrical charge (the technical term is *ionized*), for example, suggests that the electrons which it contains may readily be regarded as separate particles, each of which carries a unit of charge. The process of ionization may then be viewed as the loss of one or more electrons from the atom's structure. The protons and neutrons which make up an atom's nucleus may also be regarded as particles. Yet electrons are often observed to behave as though they were waves, for example in diffraction experiments: they may be particles, but they are observed to behave as though they are in fact spread out over space.

Whatever an electron actually is, then it is something that has both wave-like and particle-like properties. This is very hard to envisage. It is as though something were two contradictory things simultaneously – both hard and soft, say. Yet can't we say that a snow-covered landscape is precisely that – both hard and soft simultaneously – in a poetic sense, at least? It is hard in the way the snow can kill plants and animals exposed to it for too long, and soft in that a landscape draped with it has all its sharp edges smoothed out and 'softened'. We are perhaps using words to describe electrons in a way analogous to the way in which a poet might use them! And, to pursue the analogy further, sub-atomic physicists speak of the entities called quarks (quarks are the entities which constitute protons and neutrons) possessing 'charm', and even 'colour'! Clearly, they do not possess either of these qualities in the way in which they are normally understood, but the terms are used metaphorically to distinguish between quarks which possess different qualities – as though they were actually coloured, for example.

The examples one might cite of scientists using poetic or metaphorical language to describe the objects they study are not limited to the field of physics, either. Organic chemists talk about 'left-handed' and 'right-handed' molecules, meaning a pair of molecules that are composed of the same atoms, but which have their component parts arranged differently in space, so that they can exist as pairs which are related to one another like an object and its mirror image – or (hence the description) like a pair of hands. Most organic molecules which have any degree of complexity can exist in at least one pair of forms of this sort: it is due to the geometric constraints which arise from carbon atoms normally forming four bonds to other atoms. Obviously, though, such molecules are not *literally* left- or right-handed. Similarly with the biological idea of the 'selfish' gene, developed by Richard Dawkins in his book of that title: if a gene is simply a part of a complicated organic chemical (deoxyribonucleic acid, DNA), as we believe it to be, then it can obviously have no concept of 'self', and it therefore cannot possibly behave 'selfishly'. The word is being used metaphorically – poetically, if you like. (Dawkins has also used metaphors in a theory which he has developed to describe the propagation of ideas. These he describes as operating on our brains in a way analogous to a computer virus operating on the software of a computer. Rather predictably, Dawkins then uses this idea in his crusade against religions, describing these as such 'viruses'. Unfortunately for Dawkins, however, his argument cuts both ways. There is surely no way of judging who is the one infected with a virus – the religious believer, the agnostic, or the atheist. All espouse culturally conditioned views, after all.)

Of course, none of this is to deny either the importance of all the concepts mentioned here, or the fact that they convey information about the things they are trying to describe. It is important to note, though, that the sciences can and do use words in non-literal ways in order to describe the objects they are investigating.

The language of theology

Now, God is not (most people would assert) something we can experience directly through our senses in a regular and predictable way. Neither, in consequence, may we describe God directly using language that is derived from our sensory experiences. Leaving aside for the moment questions of how exactly we can experience God, let's look at the sort of language that we might reasonably use to talk about him.

It is generally asserted that God is infinite – that is to say, he is not bounded or limited by any of the things which circumscribe or limit us. The first thing we need to recognize, therefore, is that there is a qualitative difference – a difference in kind – between God and us, and indeed between God and any other thing which in our experience we might wish to describe through the medium of language. Moreover, every person wishing to talk about God will have had (presumably) some personal experience of what God means to him or her, and so will be likely to have apprehended some particular aspect of the infinite nature of God. Precisely which aspect this is will depend on the particular psychological make-up of the person concerned. We are all very different as individuals, and we might expect the way in which we are psychologically disposed to make some aspects of God more intelligible to us, and some less, than other aspects. For example, God is commonly thought of as the source of wisdom, and as the source of love, and as the one who, in Christ, experienced to the full the pain and suffering of humankind. For someone who is used to wrestling with problems in a cerebral kind of way, the idea of God as one who is infinitely wise and who understands all things – the one in whom all problems have their ultimate answer – may well have a powerful appeal. To a person who is blessed with a loving and caring family background, the idea of God as the loving provider of every good thing for his children may well speak more powerfully. On the other hand, for someone whose experiences of life are less pleasant, for one who has suffered, the suffering God may speak, and may even be able to offer some comfort. We should realize that we, who are finite and limited, will only ever be able to comprehend a small part of the immensity of God. A pint glass will never be able to contain the world's oceans; and a pint glass that dips into the Atlantic in the shallows off the coast of Barbados will reveal, on analysis of its contents, very different things about those oceans from a pint glass filled with water from the depths under the Arctic ice-cap. We as individuals are analogous to pint glasses, and their contents under different circumstances are analogous to the richly varied experiences that different individuals may have of God.

Given all this, then – given that any statement we may be able to make about God will always be partial and incomplete, and may well not readily correlate with another person's understanding of God, even though their understanding may be just as relevant as our own – how may we meaningfully talk about God in such a way as to communicate our understanding to another person? I would suggest that this may properly be done in two ways.

First, we may talk not in terms of what God *is*, but rather in terms of what God *is not*. This is the type of theology known as apophatic theology:[1] it is more well established in the tradition of Eastern Orthodox theology than it is in the West. Apophatic theology recognizes that God is so great as to be beyond all descriptions that we may make of him based on our experiences of other kinds of phenomena. We may affirm that God is life, or love, or beauty; but we are ultimately obliged to admit that all the ideas we can form of life, and love, and beauty fall short of describing God in all his fullness. To say that God is love conveys a certain truth about God, but it is only a partial truth: God is actually far more than any idea of love based on our experiences as human beings can describe. In other words, we move towards God only by recognizing that our categories for understanding him are, ultimately, inadequate. Any positive statement we make about God will, ultimately, always be false, or, at the very best, only partially true. This approach to theology is sometimes called the *via negativa*, the way of negation, for obvious reasons.

By way of illustrating what I mean, here's a lovely example of this sort of thinking, from an early Christian writer named Theophilus of Antioch.

> You will say then to me, 'Do you, who see God, explain to me the appearance of God'. Hear, O man. The appearance of God is ineffable and indescribable, and cannot be seen by eyes of flesh. For in glory he is incomprehensible, in greatness unfathomable, in height inconceivable, in power incomparable, in wisdom unrivalled, in goodness inimitable, in kindness unutterable. For if I say he is light, I name but his own work; if I call him word, I name but his sovereignty; if I call him mind, I speak but of his wisdom; if I say he is spirit, I speak of his breath; if I call him wisdom, I speak of his offspring; if I call him strength, I speak of his sway; if I call him power, I am mentioning his activity; if providence, I but mention his goodness; if I call him kingdom, I but mention his glory; if I call him Lord, I mention his being judge; if I call him judge, I speak of him as being just; if I call him father, I speak of all things as being from him.[2]

Theophilus here acknowledges that all the possible descriptions of God of which he is able to think describe only single aspects of the being and activity of God, so that each of them, whilst true, fails to give an account of who or what God actually is. Descriptions are all very well, but they all fall short of giving a full account of God. If we are to make a statement about him that is actually fully true, that statement has to be a statement of what he is not: 'in glory incomprehensible, in greatness unfathomable, in height inconceivable, in power incomparable, in wisdom unrivalled, in goodness inimitable, in kindness unutterable.'

This is all very well, but we must, after all, use language if we are to try to express any ideas at all about God. The second meaningful way of speaking about God is therefore to recognize that we may meaningfully do so, if we remember that all the ways in which we may speak about God are, basically, metaphors, models or symbols. For example, we may speak of God as Father – an image that is of course a very prominent one in the Christian tradition, following Jesus' calling God his Father in the Lord's Prayer. That can be a very meaningful image to use of God, but it is no more than that – an image, a metaphor. It must not be taken too far, and recent feminist theologians are quite right to suggest that, in the past, an over-literal approach to this image, and to the language derived from it, has led to our being far too male-centred in our thinking about God. The same caution must apply when we consider the description of God riding on the wings of the wind, which we mentioned earlier in this chapter, or of that most famous of all biblical images of God – that of 'An Ancient One . . . his clothing was white as snow, and the hair of his head like pure wool' (Daniel 7. 9). Familiar as that image of God is, from pictoral art and poetry down the centuries, it is simply an image; and whilst it perhaps tells us something about God's eternal nature, or about his great wisdom, it is limited in what it can convey to us of God in his entirety. Similarly, we may speak of the universe as God's creation, and, indeed, we may believe that it is, but that is only to give a model of the relationship that exists between God and the universe as we are able to observe it. We may speak of God as present in his Church in the sacraments of Baptism and Holy Communion, or in the preaching of his word, but God himself is far greater than these symbols of his presence with his Church – though that does not by any means make his presence in them any less 'real' for the individual churchgoer who experiences them.

Paradoxes and contradictions

An important sub-group of this sort of use of images about God is the use of non-sense or paradox. For some, the idea that paradoxes – statements that are obviously self-contradictory – can impart truth might seem preposterous, and so the inconsistencies and contradictions that we find in the Bible are sometimes pointed to by them as indicating that the Bible is not to be taken seriously. We have seen that different books of the Bible frequently present very different understandings of God, and they might therefore be expected to contradict one another in some respects. Such instances may be said to be external contradictions of texts – cases where one text is contradicted by another, from a different book. The biblical texts also contain some internal contradictions, places where a single book appears to be saying two different things. An example of this may be seen in St John's Gospel, according to which Jesus said both 'The Father and I are one' (10. 30) and 'The Father is greater than I' (14. 28), two statements which appear to contradict one another. Taken together, and taken literally, these sayings may not make sense; but when we go a bit deeper we may see that a certain consistency of meaning arises from them. Later Christian thought arrived at the conclusion that Jesus is both the same as, and different from, God the Father: this is given expression in the classic Trinitarian formula that the Father and the Son are of the same substance but are different persons. In a similar paradox, Jesus himself came to be considered both fully human and fully divine.

At one level, perhaps it's true to say that the *only* way we may understand God is to approach him in terms of paradoxes. Since all the statements which we can make about him are ultimately flawed, the best we can do is to hold them in tension with their own contradictions.

Different languages?

The language of theology, based largely (and of necessity) on the use of negatives and of metaphors, stories and models, may seem very different to the language of science. However, I believe that in both of these areas we may see significant ways in which the languages of the sciences and of theology may come together and overlap.

1. THE WAY OF NEGATION

We have seen that one of the greatest analyses of what constitutes science – the analysis of Karl Popper – has defined scientific as opposed to non-scientific statements in terms of their being falsifiable. The way towards scientific truth, in this view, lies – paradoxically, it may seem – through the way of statements that are, ultimately, untrue. A statement like 'The velocity of light is 2.998×10^8 ms^{-1}' is (in Popper's analysis) deemed scientific because it is possible to prove it false: more accurate measurement will result in a closer approximation to the real value of this constant. In other words, a truer statement is 'The velocity of light is *not* (quite) 2.998×10^8 ms^{-1}'; and it is *this* statement, in fact, which conveys scientific information to us. The parallels with the approach of apophatic theology shouldn't need spelling out: there, too, it is recognized that only through the medium of negatives can we arrive at statements which may definitely be said to be true. For example, to say 'God is wisdom' allows us only a partial insight into the nature of God, whilst to say 'God is *not* wisdom (in any way that we human beings are capable of understanding the word)' gives us actually a far truer picture of God. Of course, God is wisdom, in the same way that the velocity of light is 2.998×10^8 ms^{-1} – in the sense, that is to say, that these are good approximations to the truth; but the deeper we go into either issue, the clearer it becomes to us that these statements are both actually false if we see them as saying *all* that needs to be said about their subjects. We might perhaps say that wisdom is one aspect of God, of which our experiences allow us some limited understanding, in the same way that velocity is one interesting aspect of light, of which our measurements give us a limited understanding.

2. THE USE OF METAPHORS AND MODELS

Here again it is possible to see a convergence of the language of science with the language of theology. We have seen that talk about God requires us continually to use metaphors and models: statements which are not literally true, but which convey aspects of the truth about God by the images they conjure up. God is a loving shepherd, a mighty ruler, a suffering servant, a father anxious for his children, a prince of peace, an 'Ancient One': none of these images is literally true, though they all convey to us metaphorically some truth about God. (In providing us with concrete images of a non-material God, they also furnish subject matter for all who work in the plastic arts.)

Models of God, and of the way in which he interacts with the world, are also commonplace: the various models of God as creator might serve as examples here. The beginning of the book of Genesis depicts God as creating the cosmos, the earth, and life upon the earth. Some, of course, would assert that the story presented there is literally true; and that would be one model for understanding God as creator. Personally, I am unhappy with that model, and find other suggestions more helpful. It is now widely held that the cosmos began with a singular (in both senses of the word) event, which is popularly known as the 'big bang'; and it has been suggested that it is in God's initiation of that event that his activity as creator is best understood. It has also been suggested that God continuously contributes to the creation of the universe, through operation of physical laws, and through the activities of the creatures which live in it, such as human beings: we are, in Philip Hefner's evocative phrase, 'Created co-creators' with God.[3] It has even been suggested, as we have seen, that the universe itself may be understood in some sense as God's body, and this suggests a whole new model for the activity of God in creation. Of course, none of these models actually conveys the entire truth; but they may all to a greater or lesser extent help us in casting light on the activity of God in creation.

We have also seen that the language of science uses metaphors; and that science continually uses models to describe the subjects it is investigating should not need to be laboured unnecessarily. Consider, as an example of a model commonly used in science, Bohr's model of the electronic ground state of a hydrogen atom: a nucleus, consisting of a positively-charged proton, orbited by a much smaller, negatively-charged electron. It is an easily visualizable model, comparable to that which we use for our solar system – a massive sun orbited by a much smaller planet.

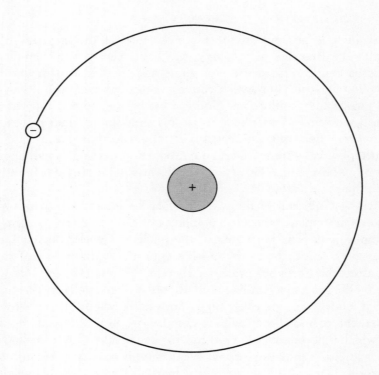

FIG.1: The Bohr model of the hydrogen atom

Experiments have shown that Bohr's model of the hydrogen atom is not actually true (the most probable location for the electron in its ground state is not somewhere on an orbit at a fixed distance from the nucleus, but is actually at the nucleus itself!). However, alternatives to this model are difficult to visualize, so it remains of considerable value. It is still frequently used, for example, in teaching about atomic structure, despite its not actually being true.

Paradoxes, discussed above in a theological context, also have their place in scientific theories. The famous paradox of Schrödinger's cat has already been mentioned (see Chapter 2): here's another example of a paradox, again from the strange quantum world. Electrons, as mentioned earlier in this chapter, are both waves and particles, and hence they display the properties of both. One property of waves is that they will undergo diffraction: when a barrier, in which there is a slit of width comparable to the wavelength concerned, is placed in the path of a moving wave, then the wave motion passes through the slit, and then radiates out from it, as though the slit were a point source of the wave.

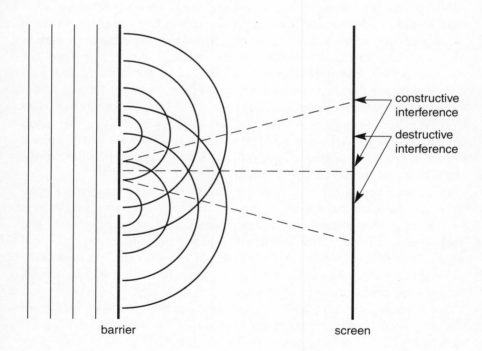

barrier   screen

FIG. 2: Interference as a result of waves being diffracted through two slits

When there is a second slit in the barrier, the two sets of waves radiating from the two slits interfere with one another, producing constructive and destructive interference: this will usually produce a characteristic pattern, which may be observed on a screen, in which areas of constructive and destructive interference alternate with each other. Figure 2 illustrates this. The solid lines represent wave crests: where these coincide, their effects combine to produce constructive interference, and where a crest coincides with a trough, they cancel each other out to produce destructive interference.

In the case of light waves passing through such a system, for example, a pattern of alternating light and dark 'fringes' is produced, corresponding to the light waves interfering constructively and destructively respectively. Similarly, when a beam of electrons is passed through such a twin-slit apparatus, the electrons interfere with one another and a pattern may be developed on a sensitive plate showing 'bright' areas where many electrons arrive at the plate and 'dark' areas where none do.

Now, what would happen if a single electron approached those slits? One would think that, as it is a particle, it would have to go through either one slit or the other. However, when this experiment is carried out in such a way that electrons approach the slits one at a time, the resulting pattern observed does not correspond to that which one would expect, showing the electrons to have passed through one slit or the other: rather, an interference pattern is obtained, as is obtained when many electrons approach the slits together. The shocking result of this observation is that those single electrons have not gone through one slit or the other – rather, they have *each* gone through *both*. A single entity, in other words, can actually be in two places at the same time!

Of course, this conclusion is really due to our understanding of electrons as 'particles-and-waves' being inadequate. Electrons are perhaps best thought of as species that under certain conditions display wave-like properties, and under other conditions display particle-like properties, but which are in fact neither one nor the other. However, since it is impossible to visualize in that case exactly what electrons might be, we are forced back on apparent paradoxes such as this one.

Interestingly, we have here a possibility for the cross-fertilization of the languages of science and theology, since it should be possible for each to borrow from the other in order to expand the range of descriptive metaphors at its disposal. As an example of science borrowing from theology, we might cite Tipler's use of the idea of resurrection in a cosmology based entirely on physics, mentioned earlier in this book.[4] As an example of a way in which theology might profitably borrow from science, consider the understanding that the Church has of Christ as one who was both fully human and fully divine. This is a very difficult paradox to try to get one's mind around, as one would expect the concept 'fully divine' to be incompatible with true humanity and the concept 'fully human' to be incompatible with true godliness. However, our understanding of this paradox may be aided by thinking once again about the properties of the electron. As we have mentioned, electrons behave as though they were both waves and particles, two things which one would also expect to be mutually exclusive. What actually happens in the case of electrons, though, is that their behaviour depends on how they are observed. If one constructs an experiment which is likely to reveal the wave-like nature of electrons, then one observes them to behave as waves: if one constructs an experiment which is likely to reveal the particle-like nature of electrons, then one will observe them to behave as particles. What one sees depends on how one looks. Perhaps the idea of Jesus as fully human and fully divine can be better understood in the light of this behaviour, since here, again, what one sees depends on how one looks. If we look to Jesus from within a human psychological framework, as providing a great example of human ethical behaviour, and as a great moral teacher, then we will see a very human figure. We may even want to follow the approach of Jung, who saw in Jesus a symbolic representation of the fully individuated human being. On the other hand, if we look to Jesus in the light of certain of the writings of the Bible, seeing him in more metaphysical terms – as, for example, the incarnation of the Word of God – then we will see a divine figure. The experiences of millions of Christians through the centuries bear testimony to the reality of that understanding for them.

Both these perceptions, then, are true; but neither is complete outside its own frame of reference, just as the description of an electron as simply a particle or simply a wave is incomplete outside the frames of reference that see electrons only in one of those ways.

A word about definitions

We all like to define things: we like to be sure that we know exactly what it is that we are discussing. All this talk about paradoxes and models and metaphors and so on may seem a little disturbing: it is as though I am fighting shy of defining things, of actually standing up and saying clearly what I mean. And in any case, surely science is really all about understanding and defining things; and so perhaps should theology be, if it is to spread its ideas around effectively and not be accused of being just so much woolly obscurantism.

Whilst I sympathize with any sense of frustration that might have been aroused by the fuzziness that has been emerging through parts of this last chapter, I believe such fuzziness to be inevitable. Some things simply cannot be defined clearly. Nice as it would be to be able to give a clear and concise answer to a question such as, 'Who (or what) is God?', I fear that it is impossible – as anyone who has seriously considered it for any time will surely agree. And it is not only theologians who are faced with a dilemma in this respect, because it is equally impossible to give a clear and concise answer to a question like 'What is an electron?' We might answer that question by saying, 'An electron is a particle having rest mass so-and-so, and charge such-and-such.' However, this answer just generates further questions. What is mass? What is charge? We might continue, 'Mass is a measure of resistance to motion: charge is a property which some entities possess, such that those having the same charge repel each other whilst those having opposite charges attract each other.' But that is in neither case to say what the property *is*, only what an entity possessing that property *does* – it resists motion, and it attracts and repels other particles. In short, it is only possible to define an electron in terms of what it does: that is to say, in terms of its effects on other entities – in terms, if you like, of its relationships.

So perhaps here, once again, we may draw parallels between the scientific and the theological issues under discussion; because if we want to attempt any definition of God, too, in terms of what he *is*, we will find the task beyond us; but if we think instead in terms of what he *does*, some form of understanding becomes possible. 'God is that being or principle which creates, sustains, and loves the universe and all it contains': whilst this statement has metaphorical elements, it does provide an approach to the question 'Who is God?' analogous to that outlined above to the question 'What is an electron?' In the same way, it answers the question in terms of what God *does*, rather than in terms of any definite statement about who or what God *is*. And of course, as believers in God have always insisted, God is always known in terms of his relationship with the believer, as an electron is known in terms of its interactions or relationships with other things which may be observed by an experimenter.

Of course, there are an infinite number of differences between God and an electron; but it is surely interesting to note the similarities in language which seem appropriate in approaching and responding to questions concerning the nature of each – questions that are of prime importance to the theologian and the physicist respectively. The methods of theologian and scientist would appear to converge at times even when we consider the language used by each.

This all might seem a little weird. Some of what I have suggested may seem to lie beyond the boundaries of traditional understandings of both science and theology. But who defines such boundaries? And by what authority? More generally, we might ask: What are the sources of tradition and authority in the sciences and in theology? And if anyone were to advocate changes in our traditional understandings, then it might well also be asked: How (if at all) do those authorities which exist allow theories to change? These are the questions we shall be addressing in the next chapter. First, though, it seems appropriate in a chapter on language to say a little about that field of human endeavour in which language is all-important – the field of literature.

Another diversion: thought experiments and poetry

'Thought experiments', we have noted, are experiments which we might like to carry out in reality, but which we are prevented from doing by our lack of adequate apparatus, or skill (or perhaps funding!). A scientist might therefore exercise his or her imagination in trying to work out what would happen to a particular system under a particular set of circumstances that are otherwise inaccessible. Similarly, one important way in which our theological understanding can advance is through such thought experiments, and in practice these are often carried out by literary means. The whole area of writing known as 'narrative theology' recognizes the value of narratives and stories in expressing and developing theological insights. In recent years, several theological writers have sought, by re-telling biblical stories from alternative perspectives, to expand our understandings of those stories.[5]

Our imaginations are very powerful tools, and the uses to which they have been put by many writers and poets down the centuries have surely advanced the way in which we think about ourselves and about our relationships, both with our environment and with God. In the field of literature, we might cite the Russian novelist F. M. Dostoevsky, who has already been mentioned in this book, as an example of an author who wrote much about God and about how people relate to him – and about the consequences of their failing to do so. In novels like *Crime and Punishment* and *The Possessed* Dostoevsky wrote of people who found their lives destroyed by their attempts to assume moral responsibilities they were unable to bear. Jesus and the Devil both appear as characters in *The Brothers Karamazov*, in separate incidents, in order to make theological and political points. Human life is discussed in *Notes from Underground* – is it utterly pointless, or shot through with potential? The possibility of a person possessing true humility, and the consequences of that humility in the relationships which that person then has with others, is explored in *The Idiot*.

Many other examples of such writing may readily be found. To mention just a few, earlier this century T. S. Eliot provided comments on the spiritual condition of his age, relating it to past Christian tradition through his frequent references to the writings of Dante and others, in his famous poem *The Waste Land*. In our own day the Welsh poet R. S. Thomas explores both religious and secular themes, and the relationships between them, in his poetry. One of his books of poems is entitled *Experimenting with an Amen*, a title which in itself brings together delightfully the scientific and religious world-views. Another Russian writer, Leonid Borodin, has fascinatingly explored issues such as the occurrence of miracles, and the redemptive power of suffering, in his novels and short stories.[6] Many other examples of such theological experimentation in works of literature might be cited.

In general, it might be said that the use of metaphors, as described earlier in this chapter, to describe those things to which our languages give us either limited access or none, constitutes the very stuff of literature in general and of poetry in particular. Poetry is surely an art form that is all about using words to point beyond themselves to some greater reality which words used literally and 'correctly' cannot begin to approach. And not only can the content of the words achieve this, but they may also be put together in such a way that the very sounds that they make when spoken give rise to music, enabling them to speak directly to our subconscious in the way that many people find that music itself can also do. Indeed, the idea that spiritual messages might be conveyed through the medium of music goes right back to the very earliest years of the Church, and still further back than that in other religious traditions. In the last few years, the great popularity of composers such as Arvo Pärt and John Tavener – the former of whom frequently sets liturgical texts, and the latter of whom goes so far as to describe his musical compositions as 'ikons' – would appear to testify to its continuing power to do so. Music, like literature, can be a forum in which theological ideas are advanced. Bishop Richard Harries has gone so far as to write: 'All works of art, whatever their content, have a spiritual dimension.'[7] Poetry, and music, and the representational arts too, can all be important experimental tools by which we may explore and develop our understandings of God, in a way that is perhaps complementary to that in which the methods of the sciences explore and develop our understandings of ourselves and of the physical universe.

Moreover, in our practical relating to God through the activities of prayer and meditation we are often taking part in a process akin to poetry, in which words are used imprecisely, in order to engage with a reality greater than they are able fully to encompass. The process of searching for meaningful models and analogies for God, accurately reflecting human experiences of him, and of engaging meaningfully with him in prayer, occupied many biblical and post-biblical authors in the past. This search can and should be carried out in the same way in our own day; and it has moreover to use the same tool – language – that has always been used.

This type of exploration is not limited solely to theological perspectives. Our understandings of the nature of human beings are also important in our thinking about spiritual issues, and the literary 'thought experiment' lends itself equally well to anthropological speculation as to theological. There is a well-known and particularly interesting example of this, which happened when two great writers independently and more or less simultaneously wrote plays which explored the possibility of people living to a great age. Would it be a good or a bad thing for a human being to live to be many hundreds, or even thousands, of years old? One writer, George Bernard Shaw, wrote a play called *Back to Methuselah*, in which he speculated that longevity would bring about great happiness and contentment, as people became very wise and understanding of one another and of their environment. 'One moment of the ecstasy of life as we live it would strike you dead', says one of the 'Ancients' to a younger character in part five of Shaw's play.[8] The other writer, the Czech author Karel Čapek, reached completely the opposite conclusion in his play *The Makropulos Secret*. A woman in that play has lived to be over 300 years old, and has discovered that such an existence as hers is meaningless: nothing has any value any more. Although she has remained outwardly young and beautiful, she speaks thus of her existence to those around her: 'One cannot stand it . . . one's soul dies.'[9] Through the fascinating contrast of outlooks which they provide, these two plays both cast some imaginative light on the debate over whether or not human longevity would be a good thing. They cannot resolve the issue, but they can deepen our understanding of the complexities involved in it, and so I think it appropriate to describe them as thought experiments.

The relevance of poetry and similar art forms to science is not so easy to perceive. The story has been told of a scientist in the years prior to the last war who habitually published his work in papers written in heroic couplets, although, as one might expect, he was regarded within the scientific community as something of an eccentric. Scientists might not need to use language in a poetic fashion – after all, they have a highly developed technical vocabulary in which they are able to attempt to give unequivocal expression to their subject matter – but perhaps in terms of the way in which they think they might learn something from poetry, for example from the way in which poetry can bring about unexpected juxtapositions of ideas. It is frequently by

bringing ideas together in unexpected ways that science moves forward.

The quotation at the head of this chapter is from a poem that has
been found inspirational and life-enhancing by thousands of people in the
centuries since it was written. I quoted it in the original Italian since this
is a chapter about language, and I wanted to use it to make two points.

First, languages which we are unable to speak can appear meaningless.
This can be a problem for anyone wishing to begin studying a subject which
is new to them, and not only if the subject in question is a foreign language.
Most academic disciplines use a specialized vocabulary and syntax: this is
true both of the sciences and of an 'arts' subject such as theology. If true
dialogue between people who speak different languages is to occur, it is
imperative that both make efforts to learn the vocabulary and grammar of
the other. This is as true for people from different academic disciplines as
it is for those from different countries.

Second, it follows from this that an awful lot of our intellectual labour
must, of necessity, be devoted to translation of one sort or another. We
need to be aware, too, that translation may very well involve an element
of compromise: it may be impossible to convey the full meaning of a
statement, with all the subtle nuances it may carry, when it is translated
from its original language. Dante's words, which he utters when he is
confronted by the majesty of God, have been rendered into English thus:

> How little I've said, and yet untrue!
> For that which I've seen, I hold the view,
> Cannot be said in words so few.[10]

How unsatisfactory, indeed, any translation of Dante's words is likely to
prove. The sense of inadequacy which he felt when trying to translate the
vision which he had seen into words must, surely, parallel the frustration
felt by anyone who tries to describe abstract ideas or feelings in words, or
who tries to translate words from one language into another. Indeed, who
can have tried to use words *in any way whatsoever*, and not occasionally
felt something of the frustration to which Dante alludes?

NOTES

1. See Roberta Bondi's article 'Apophatic Theology' in *A New Dictionary of Christian
    Theology*, eds Alan Richardson and John Bowden (SCM, 1983), p. 32.
2. Theophilus of Antioch to Autolycus, book 1, chapter III. I quote the translation of
    Marcus Dods from *The Ante-Nicene Fathers* series, vol. II (T. & T. Clark, reprinted
    1989).

3. See P. Hefner's essay 'The Evolution of the Created Co-Creator', in *Cosmos as Creation*, ed. T. Peters (Abingdon Press, 1989), p. 211 ff.

4. This idea may be found in F. J. Tipler, *The Physics of Immortality*. See above, Chapter 1, note 2.

5. As an example of narrative theology, see Gerd Theissen's *The Shadow of the Galilean*, trans. J. Bowden (SCM Press, 1987). This scholarly work about Jesus is cast in the form of a novel, set at the time of Christ, narrated by a Galilean merchant named Andreas. Jesus himself never appears in the novel, but his shadow – the effects he has on others – is omnipresent. Sara Maitland has also written memorable re-tellings of biblical stories.

   On this subject in general, see John Bowden's article 'Narrative Theology' in *A New Dictionary of Christian Theology*, op. cit. p. 391.

6. Leonid Borodin's captivating writing may be sampled in his novels *The Year of Miracle and Grief* (Quartet Books, 1984) and *The Third Truth* (Collins Harvill 1989), and, most especially, in *The Story of a Strange Time*, a collection of short stories (Collins Harvill, 1990).

7. R. Harries, *Art and the Beauty of God* (Mowbray, 1993), p. 101.

8. G. B. Shaw, *Back to Methuselah* (Penguin, 1987), p. 253.

9. K. Čapek, *The Makropulos Secret*, trans. Y. S. Graff and R. T. Jones, in the Čapek anthology *Toward the Radical Centre* (Catbird Press, 1990), p. 173. Čapek's play is perhaps best known in English-speaking countries as the basis of Janáček's opera of the same title.

10. I am very grateful to Martin and Carol Haddrill for this translation of Dante.

7

Authority, tradition and change

One of the best regulations you have is the one which forbids any young man to enquire into the relative merits of the laws; everyone has to agree, with one heart and voice, that they are all excellent.

Plato, *The Laws*, book 1

In the three related areas of authority, tradition and attitude to change, once again there seems to me to be a common perception of science and religion as greatly different to one another. That perception might be characterized as follows. In the sciences, there is no recognized absolute authority, which must approve new discoveries if they are to be considered valid: tradition likewise plays little role in the development of science; and changes in our scientific understanding come about regularly, and are a part of the free-flowing endeavour of science. On the other hand, a religion like Christianity has recognized and inflexible sources of authority to which it subscribes – the Bible, and the teachings of the Church: it is straitjacketed by an immovable and frequently rather arcane set of traditions; and, as a result of all this, it is almost completely resistant to change. The oft-trumpeted cries of 'irrelevant' directed at the Church today presumably arise from such an understanding of it as a fossilized relic from the past, unable to adapt to contemporary ways of viewing the world.

Let us contrast these perceived attitudes of science and theology to a single piece of new data. What would happen if a novel type of particle were to be discovered through observations made in the course of a new experiment, or a new story about Jesus were to be discovered from an ancient source that is not included in the canonical Gospels?[1] Science, it might be maintained, submits to no authority: the datum, if it has been collected and analysed carefully enough, is not required to conform to any particular model (it might be *expected* to fit into the model on the basis of which the experiment was set up in the first place, but there is no *requirement* for it to do so), and so our proposed new particle will be immediately accepted. On the other hand, the novel story about Jesus is circumscribed by a great weight of authority. For it to be accepted, it must fit in with other biblical texts, and with the previous teaching of the Church. If it does not do so, this will undermine any authority the new story might otherwise have, and possibly even lead to its suppression. Tradition has a role to play in this process too: the Church has a great weight of tradition that appears hard to budge and which might weigh heavily against the acceptance of any new datum (or which, on the other hand, may not, and may hasten unnaturally its acceptance), whilst science appears to have no such weight of past observations fettering the interpretation of novel data.

In short, it would appear that science is always ready to progress, to accommodate new information, whilst a religious system is very resistant to change of any sort. An outmoded scientific theory – a theory which can no longer be accommodated within the scientists' understanding of how the universe works – is swiftly jettisoned when a new and better theory which also fits the facts comes along: we have already looked at examples such as that of phlogiston in this respect (see Chapter 2). On the other hand, an outmoded theological idea – a theory about God, perhaps, which no longer makes much sense – is held on to, even if there is an overwhelming amount of evidence opposed to it, as though there were some kind of virtue in simply clinging to something for the sake of it. These are of course caricatures; but perhaps, as can sometimes be the case with caricatures, there are one or two uncomfortable elements of truth contained within them.

Authority and tradition in theology

Now, in the case of theology there are indeed authorities, arbiters in what is or is not to be considered a legitimate theory. The Bible is reckoned by all Christians to be their principal source of authority, although of course like any other set of texts the Bible is open to a variety of interpretations. In deciding what is and what is not a legitimate interpretation of it, the Church has assumed responsibilities too; and so the Church has had, and continues to have, a major role in defining theological theories, and in teaching them (the very word 'doctrine', in fact, means 'teaching': a 'doctor' originally meant someone empowered to teach).

Incidentally, it might be worth adding at this point a word about what 'The Church' actually means. The word comes from the Greek *ekklesia*, which means not a building, or a denomination, as the word 'church' has largely come to mean, but rather a local gathering of people. It cannot be too strongly emphasized that the proper understanding of the Christian Church should be in terms of such gatherings of Christian people. These gatherings perform a variety of different functions: from praying to and praising God, and debating theological issues, to doing practical work to help the poor and needy. (In the days of the Roman Empire, when the Church was first set up, there were no social services, and much work looking after the needy in society was done by and through the auspices of the Church. That charitable work is, of course, still very much part of the Church's work in the world today.)

The ideas about God and about Christ which are held by the Church are not arbitrary: they are the result of discussions and debate which has been carried out through centuries in such gatherings of Christians, involving the insights of many thousands of people, some of whom are remembered by name but most of whom probably are not. The Church therefore represents what one writer has called a 'well-winnowed tradition': that is to say, it has been 'tested and sifted for effectiveness through time and in experience'.[2] An individual, or even a group of individuals, who wishes to disagree with a centuries-old tradition of this sort should therefore not do so lightly. Ultimately, the understandings of God and of Christ that have come to be considered as authoritative by the Church have been reached chiefly through the decisions made by representative councils which have met to consider such issues. These councils include the 'ecumenical councils' of the early Church, as well as more recent manifestations of decision-making bodies in present-day Churches of different denominations. Thus orthodoxy in the Church has not come about through the arbitrary whims of a few individuals: rather, it is a consensus of many voices arrived at over a lengthy period of time, and of trial and testing.

Here's an example of how this sort of approach to decision-making in doctrinal matters works in practice. The traditional Christian understanding of God is that he is to be thought of as the Holy Trinity: God is said to be one, but also three – Father, Son and Holy Spirit. This rather odd and counter-intuitive understanding of God was arrived at because Christians wished very much to affirm, along with the Jews from whom their religion had derived so much, that God was one; and yet they believed also that

Jesus was also in some sense God. Part of Christian experience has always been the presence of the Holy Spirit with and in the Church; and it was clearly necessary for this Spirit to be seen as being God, too. But all this talk made it seem as though Christians believed, effectively, in three Gods. How could the strict monotheism that Christianity professed be defended against this charge?

The response to this theological dilemma grew gradually out of the experiences of Christians in the first four or five centuries CE, and was given classic expression by a group of fourth-century Church leaders, who are known as the Cappadocian Fathers (Basil of Caesarea, his friend Gregory of Nazianzus, and Basil's brother, Gregory of Nyssa). The doctrine was established that God is one substance (Greek *ousia*) and three persons (Greek *hypostaseis*). These Greek words were used in the philosophy of that day. Initially they meant more or less the same thing: the substance of something – its real nature, that which 'stands beneath' the mere appearance of a thing (this is the literal meaning of *hypostasis*). After these words had had their meanings refined in Christian debate, however, *ousia* came to mean the substance of something, in the sense of its underlying reality, whilst *hypostasis* came to refer to the specific instance of an entity in which that reality is given expression: in a document that has come down to us as one of Basil's letters (but which in fact was probably written by Gregory of Nazianzus), the example is given of *ousia* referring to mankind in general whilst *hypostasis* refers to individual people, 'Peter' or 'John'.[3] So, the classic Christian understanding of God came to be formulated in terms of God being one in *ousia*, three in *hypostaseis*.

Well, that sort of understanding of God is all well and good for those with the time, the energy and the inclination to pursue a study of Greek philosophy; but in the late twentieth century it must seem to many to be rather an esoteric way of thinking about God. Indeed, since there are no longer any other things in our world or in our experience that we think about philosophically or technically in terms of their 'substance', and since we do in fact use the words 'substance' and 'person' in other, non-technical senses, it might well be argued that this understanding of the Trinity could well do with being either quietly set aside, or else radically re-interpreted for our own age.

Various suggestions have been made down the ages for thinking about the Trinity, which have by-passed the philosophy used in its original definition. Perhaps the most famous example of a way in which to conceive of the Trinity is that of St Patrick, who is said to have taught the Irish people, amongst whom he was working as a missionary, about God the Holy Trinity by using as his model the shamrock. This plant has three leaves, like a clover, and yet is one plant. There are other models which have been drawn from nature for thinking about the Trinity: for example, it has also been thought of as analogous to a spring, a river and a lake, which are all different, but to all of which is given the name 'water'; or as analogous to the trunk, roots and branches which constitute a tree. Another way in which the Trinity is sometimes conceived is in terms of a love relationship: Father and Son, the lover and the beloved, united by the Holy Spirit as the bond of love that exists between them, a bond so strong that it fully unites all three, to the extent that talk of one God is actually the best way of describing what's going on. (These particular approaches to the Trinity, incidentally, were all developed by St Augustine.[4]) And there are many other ways of thinking about the Trinity.

A recent example of further exploration in this area is provided by a Church of England Doctrine Commission's report entitled *We Believe in God*. This report notes that 'In modern theology . . . there is a good deal to militate against belief in the doctrine of an eternally triune God', and that 'Most Christians would probably say that their experience of God is not obviously or immediately perceived as Trinitarian in structure.'[5] On these grounds, one might well query the continued relevance of the doctrine of the Holy Trinity. However, the authors of the report go on to describe a modern approach to God which does in fact conform to a Trinitarian model. They describe the Christian experience of prayer as 'Being brought to the Father through incorporation into the Son by the power of the Holy Spirit.'[6] As Christians pray, they journey towards and into the being of God the Father. That journey is experienced through their becoming inwardly more Christ-like, and through their being joined to 'the body of Christ', the Church (see 1 Corinthians 12. 12 ff.). And this entire process is directed and facilitated by the Holy Spirit.

This is a fascinating example of the use of practical experience in the here-and-now to support the validity of past theoretical teachings. Indeed, present-day experience might perhaps usefully be regarded as the 'acid test' for any such doctrines. The words used by the Doctrine Commission might not make a lot of sense to anyone who has seldom or never attempted to pray; but I suspect that many of those who have done so from positions within the Christian tradition will recognize the validity of this model, and agree that, as the Commission's report suggests, reflection on prayer does indeed point towards an empirical verification of the classic ideas of God as three in one.

I believe that this sort of 'earthing' of a doctrine in the practical experiences of Christian believers is to be wholeheartedly applauded for the new lease of life it breathes into an idea, like that of the Trinity, that might otherwise run the risk of being reckoned little more than an academic irrelevance. Note, also, that like the earlier formulations of the Trinity in terms of Greek philosophy, this new understanding is the work not of any individual but rather of a group of Christians pooling their understandings and experiences. This example is perhaps not untypical of the way in which Christian theological understanding has been developed in the past; and it shows an exciting and valuable way in which that understanding can be developed yet further in the present and in the future, through bodies within the Church continually debating afresh matters defined by authoritative councils in the past.

If a much-valued and cherished theological idea were to have been challenged in the past, it would have been quite probable that Church leaders would have summarily quashed the challenge. These days, many Church leaders, within all the main denominations, are much more reluctant to stifle speculation, or theological novelty. This can only be a good thing. When all is said and done, it will always be quite beyond our capacities to understand God fully; and, moreover, God's revelation of himself to humankind is presumably a continuous thing, in which will be reflected the ever-accumulating experiences of humankind. It therefore follows that any static picture of God is inevitably a false picture. The Christian theological tradition should constantly be ready to grow and to develop its understanding of God.

Authority and change in the sciences

We have seen that authority in theological issues exists in the Church, although the exercise of that authority tends not to be exclusively in the hands of individuals. There is unquestionably no precisely equivalent source of authority in the case of the sciences – nothing that is the equivalent of, say, the Church of England Doctrine Commission, or still less the Roman Catholic Magisterium. However, there *are* sources of authority in the sciences as well as in theology; and these can potentially be just as oppressive as theological authorities have been in the past.

Suppose a really radical new discovery is made, or is alleged to have been made, by a young doctoral student, who is doing his or her research under an unknown lecturer at one of the new universities in Britain. (I should add that I do not know of such a case as I am about to describe, but I see no reason why it should not happen.) A research paper is eagerly written and sent to an appropriate scientific journal for publication. Once there, an editor will have it read, usually by at least a couple of referees who are experts in the relevant area. Now suppose that those referees believe the idea to be crackpot. Perhaps at a first glimpse it indeed appears bizarre; or perhaps it refutes an idea one of them cherishes; or perhaps one of them harbours a certain resentment against the person supervising our student's research. The fact that the student is an 'unknown', with no proven ability at research, will mean that they can easily return a verdict that the paper should not be published. Now, one might say that the referees are simply being scrupulous: ideas need to be carefully backed up, particularly if they are strikingly novel, and it is obviously going to be helpful if they have the support of recognized authorities. Failing this, there is a justifiable caution in not leaping to overturn established ideas.

But *supposing that the new ideas are true*? What has effectively happened is that the weight of authority – the weight of traditional interpretation of a subject – has caused the suppression of a new scientific idea, at least in the short term. (In the longer term, a lack of published results will mean that research directed by our student's supervisor will probably not receive further funding, and research in the area where the novel result was obtained will therefore cease. This too may be perceived as the operation of authority, albeit from a different source, in suppressing novel scientific research.) Analogous sources of authority and tradition to those which obtain in the field of theological speculation therefore operate in the field of science too: the authority being simply the collective voices of senior scientists who are called upon to referee the work of others, and the tradition being simply the paradigm currently operating in the particular science concerned. It would not be particularly surprising if scientists were reluctant to see theories which have served them well disappear before the face of a challenge from an untried junior colleague (despite the urgings of Popper!). A reluctance to change is common in every field of human activity. However, it is nevertheless the case that scientists should in fact be fully prepared to see precisely that happen, if the progress of science is furthered as a result.

Here are a couple of examples, which show scientists behaving with (as it turned out) appropriate and inappropriate degrees of caution. A few years ago, some physicists announced that they had managed to achieve 'cold fusion' – nuclear fusion reactions taking place in ordinary laboratory conditions, in water at more or less room temperature. Now, nuclear fusion – the process whereby small atomic nuclei, such as those of hydrogen, are fused together, generating vast quantities of energy in the process – has often been thought of as the energy form of the future. It does not produce toxic waste by-products, which nuclear fission reactions do (nuclear fission involves large heavy atoms such as those of uranium: it forms the basis of the reactions which take place in nuclear power stations). However, fusion had only ever been observed to occur under conditions involving extremely high temperatures, which makes it a very uneconomical process. The announcement that it had occurred at lower and more manageable temperatures therefore generated a good deal of excitement – mingled with a good deal of scepticism – amongst other scientists. Such a find, entirely flying in the face of accepted ideas, and completely inexplicable by any known theory, was viewed with a good deal of suspicion.

What had happened was that some scientists had observed unaccountably high amounts of energy being produced in an experiment, and further investigations had led them to the conclusion that the only possible source of this energy was a fusion reaction. Other scientists maintained that this was impossible. Numerous other research groups tried to reproduce the results the first group of scientists had obtained, without success. Such was the furore that the story hit the national newspapers and television news reports. Eventually, however, it was pronounced that the 'find' could not be verified, and that it was therefore to be disregarded.

Now, in this case the scientists concerned were, it appears, quite justified in their scepticism. I'm not sure whether or not the reason why the original unusual results were obtained has yet been satisfactorily explained: however, clearly the scientific orthodoxy which maintained that cold fusion was an impossibility under the conditions of this experiment has been upheld (so far!). Accepted authorities, and the tradition that had led to their being in place, had decreed that cold fusion was not possible, and the scientific establishment devoted considerable energy for a brief period to re-establishing the fact. At least in this instance the original results were made public first, before they were refuted.

A lengthier resistance to change in the scientific hierarchy, albeit a resistance that was finally overcome, is cited by James Gleick in his book *Chaos*. This work charts the origins and development of the movement in the physical sciences that was eventually given the catchy, if slightly misleading, name of Chaos Theory. Gleick writes,

> Every scientist who turned to chaos early had a story to tell of discouragement or open hostility. Graduate students were warned that their careers could be jeopardised if they wrote theses in an untested discipline ... Those who recognised chaos in the early days agonised over how to shape their thoughts and findings into publishable form. Work fell between disciplines – for example, too abstract for physicists yet too experimental for mathematicians ... As the chaos specialists

spread, some departments frowned on these somewhat deviant scholars; others advertised for more. Some journals established unwritten rules against submissions on chaos; other journals came forth to handle chaos exclusively.[7]

What are we witnessing in this account of Gleick's if it is not the actions of an establishment, having its own traditions and exercising its own authority? Scientists in this novel area faced 'discouragement or open hostility' and were told 'their careers could be jeopardised'. They tried to find a 'publishable form' for their ideas – the ideas could not just be presented to the wider scientific community as they stood. Existing mainstream departments 'frowned on' them: existing journals operated a policy of excluding them. It all sounds like the response which might have greeted a priest or theologian in years gone by as a result of their questioning some accepted theological doctrine.

Of course, the authority and tradition of the Church have undoubtedly on occasion in the past weighed oppressively on new ideas, and I would not wish to deny that such oppression in theological circles has been both heavier and more censorious in the past than any which has prevailed within the sciences. But I hope that I have demonstrated that differences in attitude in these two disciplines in this area are once again differences of scale rather than of kind. In any established body, there is inevitably an innate conservatism and resistance to change. If science is sometimes guilty of resisting progress and suppressing novelty, even if it does so only for a brief period of time, that is surely only to be expected since it is, fundamentally, a human endeavour – as, of course, is theology.

Change in the Church

It is undeniable that changes on theological issues are frequently resisted by the Church. Why should this be? *Can* change on theological issues come about?

Of course, there are many possible answers to the first of these questions. Cynics might say that the reason for the emphasis on unchanging tradition in the Church is so that the Church can retain its worldly wealth and authority. Others might say that the Church is simply responding to a psychological need felt by many people: a need to have something fixed and unchanging that is a part of their lives in a rapidly changing and unpredictable world. This is something that was as true in past ages as it is today. A further practical reason is that once people immerse themselves in the traditions of the Church, they frequently find them to have a relevance that is independent of the times in which they originated. The practice of various devotional exercises, for example, has persisted because people find them helpful; however, to see the relevance of such an argument as this, first-hand experience of such devotional exercises is necessary. A person kneeling and muttering a few brief phrases over and over again, punctuating them at times with the recitation of rather longer passages, whilst simultaneously moving a string of beads through their fingers, might not appear to be doing anything terribly worthwhile to anyone who had never taken the trouble ever to say the rosary themselves. That the practice of such an activity has persisted, however, is surely a powerful testimony to its abiding value to the people who take the trouble actually to do this exercise. (The fact that Pope John Paul II's recording of the rosary proved to be a best-seller would appear to confirm this, too.)

And of course the ideas of the Church *can* change. At the time when this book was being written, women had recently been ordained priests in the Church of England for the first time, a radical changing of the traditional practice of that Church. Admittedly, the road to that change was a long one, involving debate at a variety of levels from parishes upwards, and culminating in a vote at the General Synod (the Church of England's 'Parliament'); and the Church is so unused to major changes of this sort that it has happened not without a certain unhappiness in some quarters, which may take some little while to settle down. However, this example shows that change can happen, and gives us a model of how it can come about. Perhaps in this whole area of change the practice of the Church could take a leaf from the book of the practice of science, in accepting more readily the inevitability and necessity of change, whilst continuing to assess and to weigh carefully any potential changes that are actually suggested. I would certainly not like to see every aspect of the Church's life become a complete ideological free-for-all, nor to see change come about solely for change's sake. I suspect, though, that the Church's practice could certainly move closer to that of the sciences in this respect without any sacrifice of integrity being necessary.

Perhaps the greatest requirement that would need to be fulfilled in bringing about such a change in attitude would be a preparedness on the part of the Church to live with a greater variety of attitudes within it. Consider an example from the sciences like the rejection of the phlogiston theory. This idea, which was probably cherished by many who had found it to be useful and to make sense from a practical point of view, would doubtless have held the stage for some time alongside its successor (the theory, you'll remember, that it is the presence of oxygen in the air that is responsible for the phenomenon of combustion), before it finally dwindled away into the realm of being a redundant hypothesis. Clearly, no change in the views of the Church will be possible unless that period in which traditional views are allowed to co-exist with more recent ones is permitted. At the present time, a more common reaction to novel ideas in the realm of doctrine is effectively to outlaw some views, and to say that those who adhere to them place themselves outside the Church altogether. This would be analogous to saying that those who opposed the phlogiston theory placed themselves outside the boundaries of science in doing so. Well, they *might* well have been wrong (as it happens, in this case they weren't), but removing their ideas from consideration would have done no good. The truth about combustion would have been established eventually, and all that would have happened would have been that the science of the time would have been discredited.

On the other hand, what happens when a tradition within the Church is challenged? Consider the Church of England, for example. In the last century, Anglican clergy who introduced 'ritualistic' elements into services in their churches could be imprisoned under the Public Worship Regulation Act of 1874 (indeed, a number were).[8] The sort of practices concerned – placing lit candles on the altars of churches, wearing particular vestments, adorning churches with crucifixes and statues, and using fixed rather than moveable altars – were considered retrograde steps, beyond the bounds of acceptable practice at that time. However, many Anglican churches make free use of such 'ritualistic' elements in worship today, since they have been found by many to be effective aids to worship.

What about the doctrines of the Church, though, as opposed to its liturgical practices? Consider the doctrine of the Virgin Birth of Jesus, as understood literally. Those who have denied this doctrine have often been declared outside the boundaries of the Church, as the ritualists once were, and therefore no longer in a position to influence it. But what would happen if we were to say instead, 'Let's accept *as a possibility* the idea that the Virgin Birth understood literally is an unhelpful rather than a helpful doctrine, and see what happens'? Presumably, all those who wished to make a comment in this debate would, over a period of time, bring forward evidence that the position which they preferred was the most helpful to the Church at large. Those supporting the traditional doctrine might produce evidence to support the position that the Virgin Birth, understood literally, gives us an otherwise unobtainable insight into the uniqueness, the Divinity even, of Jesus. Those opposing the traditional doctrine might produce evidence to support the contention that the idea of the Virgin Birth literally understood does more harm than good, in encouraging superstitious attitudes within the Church and discouraging those outside it from taking it seriously. It might also be suggested that the best way to understand the significance of the Virgin Birth is to think of it as a myth, in the way that that word was understood in Chapter 5 of this book: to interpret it, in other words, as a story designed to tell us symbolically something about the nature of Jesus as different from all other people, a story which may or may not be true in terms of its historical veracity. A period might then ensue when people within the Church could legitimately adopt one or other of these attitudes – or indeed some other one – and debate the issues involved with their fellow Christians. After a while, if it became clear that one or other view had to prevail, a consensus as to which view it should be might then begin to emerge. On the other hand, it might be that Christians of all these views and others could quite happily live together, whatever they thought about this subject, without a definitive decision one way or the other actually having to be made – as has effectively happened in the case of ritualism in Church worship.

It might be said that having such doctrinal flexibility is an impossibly impractical way for Churches to function. Maybe this is true (although I suspect that this flexibility is in fact a lot nearer to what is actually going on in many of our churches than people outside them might think). I'm not so sure. I would want to maintain that the Church could learn a good deal from the way in which science develops, changes and, of course, *grows*; and in doing so, it could become more open to the change and growth of doctrines itself. In this respect, it is encouraging to see that many Churches, of widely varying denominations, do now actively encourage a degree of experimentation within themselves. This experimentation may be practical, in terms of liturgical and devotional practices, or theoretical, in terms of theological speculation. Innate conservatism, in the Church as in any other institution, will always weigh for stasis and against change; but think how many of the great benefits which science has brought us could not have happened if all purely speculative science were to have been discouraged or suppressed. Some – indeed, most – scientific speculation will ultimately turn out to be fruitless; but the tiny proportion that doesn't can bring changes of great richness and profundity. When the Church has undergone change in the past, comparable enrichments of our understanding have been the result; and there seem to be no reasons why future changes should not be just as beneficial.

Both the sciences and theology, then, are practised within a framework which accepts an authority, and has a tradition to which current theory and practice must inevitably relate. Change can come about in either discipline, although doubtless rather more readily in the case of science. Once again, perceived differences between the two disciplines turn out to be differences of scale rather than differences of kind when we examine the issues concerned.

Let us now bring this discussion to a conclusion by drawing together some of the threads of the argument so far.

NOTES

1. There are in fact several ancient Gospels, relating alleged sayings of Jesus and incidents from his life which are not found in the Gospels we possess. Many of them are demonstrably late works, recounting bizarre and unedifying material about Jesus (and, in addition, frequently expanding a good deal on what we know from more orthodox sources about the life of his mother, Mary). In general, they cannot be given too much credence as throwing new light on Jesus. Literature of this sort includes the Gospel of Thomas (a collection of Jesus' sayings: it has been argued that this work may actually be as old as the Gospels we possess), the Gospel of Nicodemus, the Gospel of pseudo-Matthew, the Dialogue of the Savour and the Apocryphon of James. They have been translated by Alexander Walker in *The Ante-Nicene Fathers* series, vol. VIII (T. & T. Clark, reprinted 1989), and by a variety of translators in *The Other Gospels*, ed. Ron Cameron (Lutterworth Press, 1983).
2. John Bowker, *Licensed Insanities* (Darton, Longman and Todd, 1987), p. 7. This excellent piece of contemporary Christian apologetic literature is heartily recommended. Incidentally, the expression 'well winnowed' in this context was coined by the American psychologist Donald Campbell.
3. See St Basil's Epistle 38, available in the Loeb Classical Library edition of his letters (vol. I), and in *The Nicene and Post-Nicene Fathers*, second series, vol. 8 (T. & T. Clark, reprinted 1989). St Gregory of Nazianzus' 'Theological Orations', which deal *inter alia* with Trinitarian themes, may be found in volume 7 of this series, and St Gregory of Nyssa's treatise 'On the Holy Trinity' may be found in volume 5.
4. For the water and tree analogies, see St Augustine's 'On Faith and the Creed', chapter 9, and for the analogy with love, see his 'On the Trinity', book VIII, chapter 10. Both these works are translated in *The Nicene and Post-Nicene Fathers*, first series, vol. 3 (T. & T. Clark, reprinted 1988).
5. The Church of England Doctrine Commission, *We Believe in God* (Church House Publishing, 1987), pp. 106–7.
6. Ibid., p. 116.
7. J. Gleick, *Chaos*, (Penguin Books, 1988), pp. 37–8.
8. See A. R. Vidler, *The Church in an Age of Revolution* (Pelican, 1974), chapter 14. This book is volume 5 of the *Pelican History of the Church*, an excellent series recommended to anyone who wishes to explore aspects of Church history from the earliest days down to the present.

Conclusion

*I regard profound problems as I do a cold bath – quick
in, quick out.*
                    Friedrich Nietzsche, *The Joyous Science*

The story so far

The reader will be aware that in this book we have only touched,
in a not terribly systematic way, on a number of enormous and very
profound issues. I hope you will follow up this introduction to the area
of the relationship between science and theology using the books that are
referred to in the notes at the end of each chapter: *pace* Nietzsche, I
believe there is perhaps *something* to be said for prolonged and systematic
study of profound areas of thought!

There's very little in this book that will strike academic scientists
or theologians as especially remarkable. However, the publicly perceived
antipathy between these two disciplines seems to me so great, and the mis-
understandings regarding the natures of them both so deeply entrenched,
that to the non-specialist certain of my remarks may have sounded rather
strange or unusual. Let me therefore recap a few of the conclusions reached
in the course of this discussion.

I have suggested that science is not a purely rational, objective quest
that establishes once-and-for-all fact, but that it proceeds in ways that may
be far less clear-cut and rational, and rather more 'woolly', yielding *models*
of reality that gain ever greater accuracy without ever reaching absolute
perfection. Theology, too, combines rational and non-rational, objective
and subjective factors, and reaches conclusions that are best regarded as
provisional.

I have suggested that both scientific and theological understandings

143

of human beings, and their place in and relationship to the cosmos as a whole, can benefit from the insights provided by the other discipline.

I have suggested that science and theology both use rich varieties of sources, leading to their being more complicated fields of study than is sometimes realized.

I have suggested that there are aspects of the Bible that should be understood as myths – stories which may well be true, but the truth of which does not necessarily lie in their giving an historically accurate account of the past. Rather, their truth is to be sought in the effect which they have in people's lives in the present: their historicity is an irrelevance. Science, too, can both generate myths and benefit from the use of them, as they provide a sense of cohesion, of belonging to a community, for practising scientists.

I have suggested that in terms of their uses of language – for example, in their uses of models and of metaphors – science and theology are in fact more similar than different. Each uses these devices, and each on appropriate occasions may even use language normally thought of as appropriate to the other. Specialist vocabularies apart, the differences between them are largely differences of scale of usage, not of usage *per se*. Science may learn from theology in terms of the free exercise of our imaginative and intuitive faculties that the latter sometimes encourages.

I have suggested that the 'doing' of either science or theology does not take place in a vacuum, but that rather the endeavours of both scientists and theologians are conducted against a background of expectation, and are subject to the criticisms of accepted authorities.

I have suggested that theology should, like science, move progressively forward, and should not be afraid to alter or even to shed theories or doctrines if these prove to be too problematic, or too incredible, to an age far removed in time from that in which they were originally formulated.

And I have suggested that continued antagonism between scientists and religious believers cannot be justified either on scientific or religious grounds. It is, rather, the product of 'fundamentalist' attitudes which may be held for a variety of reasons, from mistaken idealism to personal insecurity. Such attitudes may be very difficult to change, but that should not prevent us from trying to do so.

If your outlook is a Christian one, I hope you have found in this book something that has prompted you to probe a bit deeper into your faith. If your outlook is indifferent or even hostile to Christianity, I hope that you have been challenged to think seriously about the Christian outlook, and in particular about how it relates to your own. Too often religious beliefs in the late twentieth-century West have been pilloried as inconsequential, irrational and out-of-date. So, in some instances, they may have been; but hardly any more so than the allegedly 'scientific' views of some of their detractors. Religious belief has been decried as child-like or infantile, but the great advances in religious understanding made by philosophers and theologians are disregarded, or condemned as too complicated.[1] Is this not a rather inconsistent attitude to take – to maintain that something is too simplistic to command respect, whilst ignoring all the work that has been done to advance our understanding of it?

Christianity has been written off at regular intervals for at least the last three hundred years, particularly during the post-Enlightenment period. The criticisms levelled at it have sometimes been just ones. However, it is my firm belief that insofar as Christianity remains true to the ideas of its originator it will remain a powerful force in the world.

Atoms and icons

In conclusion, let me return to the title of this book, chosen in order to throw into juxtaposition two 'worlds' of thinking that are normally not associated with one another. The word 'atom' tends to be used by those wishing to express themselves in terms of a scientific understanding of the world: the word 'icon' by those who perceive other layers of meaning in things, beyond the purely material. I'd like now to take these two concepts, the atom and the icon, one step further.

It seems to me that, in common with everything else in the universe, we human beings are both atoms and icons. We are atoms in that the material that comprises our bodies is comprised of atoms: atoms of carbon, hydrogen, oxygen, nitrogen, sulphur, phosphorus, and a few other elements. And we are also icons, in that in each of us it is possible to see more than the matter of which we are made. Icons have been described as 'Windows on to the divine':[2] pictures which reveal more than they themselves are by virtue of their being self-effacing, by their being transparent. Human beings can be like that, too. It is possible, indeed, to see something of God in the nature of each single entity in our cosmos, if only we look in the right kind of way. The Anglican priest and poet George Herbert put it like this:

> A man that looks on glasse,
> On it may stay his eye;
> Or, if he pleaseth, through it passe,
> And then the heav'n espie.[3]

This poem describes two different ways of looking: *at* something, or *through* it. All things are transparent, in this respect. Perhaps, ultimately, it is the task of both science and theology to sharpen our vision respectively for each of these tasks, that these two vital areas of human endeavour may share more fully in producing ever-greater understanding of ourselves and our universe. In this common task, we may perhaps see the fundamental similarity between these two intellectual disciplines at its most sharply focused, and see most sharply too their vital complementarity. It is atoms which compose the face on an icon, and it is icons which are used to represent the invisible world of the atom. We need both science and theology; and I believe most strongly that any denial of the importance of one can only serve ultimately to impoverish the findings of the other.

NOTES

1. This certainly appears to be true of Freud, whose theories about religion hinge on the idea that religion is a primitive phenomenon. Those who seek to develop religious traditions using modern philosophical criteria are accused by Freud of being 'Guilty of every possible sort of dishonesty and intellectual misdemeanour' (*The Future of an Illusion*, Penguin Freud Library vol. 12, p. 214). Freud's attitude towards religions is very clearly one of 'Heads I win, tails you lose!'
2. See Symeon Lash's article 'Icons', in *A New Dictionary of Christian Theology*, eds Alan Richardson and John Bowden (SCM, 1983), pp. 274–5.
3. This is a verse from Herbert's poem 'The Elixer'. It forms part of his great sequence of poems, 'The Temple', available in many editions (see, for example, that of C. A. Patrides (Everyman's Library, 1974), p. 188).

Glossary

anthropic principle a theory which has been expressed in a variety of ways, but which basically links the state of our universe, and the physical laws which obtain within it, with our presence in it as sentient beings, capable of observing it.

antireductionism the idea that in addition to entities possessing properties which are due to the operations of their component parts they may also have fundamentally irreducible properties that arise out of the organizational complexity which they possess. Such properties are sometimes described as *emergent* properties.

apocalyptic a literary genre (q.v.), widespread in the centuries before and just after the time of Christ, in which vivid, sometimes violent, images are used to convey messages of hope to beleaguered groups of people who (it is assumed) knew how to 'decode' the imagery used. Examples of biblical works in this style are sections of the book of Ezekiel, the latter half of the book of Daniel, and the book of Revelation.

apophatic theology theology based on the principle that, since God is far beyond human categorization, he is best talked about in terms of what he is not, rather than in terms of what he is. Also known as the *via negativa* (the way of negation).

atonement a putting at one, a reconciliation. Usually used to refer to the repairing of the breach between God and humankind achieved by Jesus.

chaos theory a slightly misleading name for the branch of mathematical physics which looks at complex behaviour in mathematically simple systems.

Church colloquially used to refer to a building, or occasionally to a denomination (e.g. the Church of England), this word originally and properly means a gathering together of people to praise God.

Church Fathers   early Christian leaders, frequently people holding positions of responsibility within the Church. Amongst the Fathers mentioned in this book are St Augustine, bishop of Hippo in North Africa in the early fifth century, Theophilus of Antioch, bishop of that city in the late second century, and the Desert Fathers (e.g. St Antony of Egypt), who were early monks devoted to leading lives of austerity away from normal human contacts.

criterion of falsifiability   the distinction between science and non-science devised by the philosopher Karl Popper, stating that only statements which are capable of being proved false may legitimately be described as scientific.

deduction   the process of reasoning that involves moving from many particular observations to a general theory which embraces them all.

deoxyribonucleic acid (DNA)   the complicated organic chemical, consisting of two interwoven chains of nucleotides, that forms the basis of genes, and hence of organic life as we know it.

determinism   the doctrine that all the events that occur in the universe are determined by the events that cause them, and that chains of causes develop according to natural laws.

dualism   in general, the understanding of things which views them in terms of opposites, e.g. good/evil, physical/spiritual, etc. In this book, the term is used most commonly when thinking about the nature of human beings. It is the idea that we are composite creatures, made up of bodies and souls (or, to put it another way, brains and minds).

emergence   *see* antireductionism.

epistemology   the theory of knowledge.

Evangelists   specifically, the writers of the four Gospels, traditionally Matthew, Mark, Luke and John (modern scholarship has suggested that these books in the form in which we possess them actually contain material from a number of different sources, and may be the work of more than one individual). More generally, any person taking it upon themselves to proclaim the Gospel, the Christian message of Good News about Jesus Christ.

form criticism   the approach to books such as the Gospels which sees them as compilations of small sayings or stories which were preserved because they were felt to be useful or important, and which seeks in consequence to determine the setting in the life of the early Church in which this importance arose.

genre a particular style of writing, having its own forms and conventions.

Gospels the first four books of the New Testament, Matthew, Mark, Luke and John, which tell of the life and death of Jesus (Luke continues his narrative in the book of the Acts of the Apostles, which tells the story of the spread of the early Church throughout the Roman Empire). The first three Gospels have many similarities – indeed, some passages in them are virtually word for word the same – which has led to their becoming known as the *Synoptic* (same view) Gospels. John's perspective is somewhat different.

holism the idea that systems should best be approached and studied in terms of wholes, rather than in terms of the parts of which they are constituted.

immanence the idea that God is present in the physical universe, pervading and indwelling all that is.

induction the process of reasoning that involves moving from a specific theory to general observations which may support or falsify that theory.

intuition/counter-intuition a process of accepting as valid reasons based on non-rational factors (feelings, emotions, etc.). Counter-intuitive factors are those which one might assess on the basis of 'feelings' to be obviously wrong, but which might in fact turn out to be right.

instrumentalism *see* non-realism.

Manicheeism a sect following the doctrines of Mani (*c.* 216–276 CE), at one time including St Augustine among their number. They subscribed to a radical dualist outlook, viewing the material world as inherently evil and in a constant state of war with the good, spiritual world.

materialism the understanding of the universe as comprised solely and exclusively of matter, there being no such thing as 'spirit'.

metaphor a way of using language in a non-literal way, describing things by analogy with some other entity or entities.

mysticism 'The direct intuition or experience of God' (Evelyn Underhill, *The Mystics of the Church*, James Clark & Co. Ltd, 1925).

natural theology theology which is based on the exercise of human reason without the aid of any revelations of himself made by God.

Newton's laws   laws of motion discovered by Sir Isaac Newton in the seventeenth century. They govern the motions and interactions of large bodies with great accuracy and were probably the inspiration for some of the more extravagantly deterministic theories that have been put forward since then. They still retain great importance for scientists and engineers, although their universal relevance has been undermined by their inapplicability at the atomic and sub-atomic levels.

non-realism   the idea that the models which we form of the physical world in response to our investigations of it are no more than that: models, artificial constructs imposed by our minds on the fundamentally unknowable stuff of the universe.

objectivity/subjectivity   the understanding of an idea as being, respectively, of universal validity or of validity only to the individual who has experienced that idea.

ontology   the study of theories of being.

panentheism   the doctrine that God is present throughout, though not fully contained within, the physical universe.

pantheism   the doctrine that more or less equates God with the physical universe.

paradigm   a framework of concepts, ideas, expectations, etc. that make up a coherent world-view, which becomes the background to all subsequent thinking by the person who subscribes to that paradigm.

Pentateuch   the first five books of the Bible, Genesis, Exodus, Leviticus, Numbers and Deuteronomy. Also known as the books of the Law, and as the books of Moses (who features prominently within them, and to whose authorship they have traditionally, although rather improbably, been ascribed).

Psalms   a sequence of poetic writings which have formed an important component of worship for both Jews and Christians since their composition. They cover a wide range of human emotions – rejoicing, thanksgiving, anger, despair. Some of them are traditionally ascribed to the ancient Jewish king, David. Non-biblical psalms also exist.

quantum physics   the branch of physics which has developed during the course of the twentieth century to account for the various peculiar phenomena that are observed in the atomic and sub-atomic domain, in which Newton's laws (q.v.) are found no longer to apply.

rationality using the faculty of reason as the basis for one's thoughts and actions.

realism the doctrine that the world revealed by our measurements during the course of scientific study is really 'out there', not just a model which we have devised or brought into being as the result of our theories.

redaction criticism the way of approaching works such as the Gospels which seeks to understand the agenda of the author(s) or editor(s) involved in their production.

reductionism the doctrine that the behaviour of whole entities may be explained and fully understood in terms of the behaviour of the parts of which they are made.

scripture literally, 'writings', but generally used to mean texts which a religious tradition considers to be sacred, vested with particular and special significance. For Christians, of course, 'Scripture' equates with 'The Bible'.

Synoptic Gospels *see* Gospels.

transcendence the idea that the reality of God lies in some sense beyond the boundaries of our world: that is, God is wholly 'other' to the physical universe.

via negativa *see* apophatic theology.

vitalism the doctrine that living things possess some non-physical 'spark' which animates them and makes them fundamentally different to inanimate matter.

wholism *see* holism.

Index